*Soon the leaflets were distributed around the hospital:*

## ARE YOU A PROFESSIONAL?

Fellow Nurses—Are you a professional? Haven't you received specialized training in one of the most arduous of all professions? Of course! Then why are your notes ignored?

Not long ago a patient almost *died* when a doctor failed to read the nurse's notes!

This is not an isolated incident. It will happen again.

A proposal has been made to integrate nurses' and doctors' notes. We must support it! "Monster Morgan" wants to keep nurses in their place.

WE ARE PROFESSIONALS. WE MUST PROTECT OUR PATIENTS!

—RANK-AND-FILE NURSES

*It was the first of the controversial leaflets—and only the beginning of the battle . . .*

# CARING

BY ANNETTE SWACKHAMER, R.N.
AND RALPH W. MOSS

BERKLEY BOOKS, NEW YORK

The characters and events in this book are based on real ones, but changes have been made to protect the privacy of the parties involved.

This Berkley book contains the complete
text of the original hardcover edition.
It has been completely reset in a typeface
designed for easy reading and was printed
from new film.

CARING

A Berkley Book / published by arrangement with
Doubleday & Company, Inc.

PRINTING HISTORY
Doubleday edition / April 1986
Berkley edition / July 1987

ISBN: 0-425-10046-4

A BERKLEY BOOK ® TM 757,375
Berkley Books are published by The Berkley Publishing Group,
200 Madison Avenue, New York, NY 10016.
The name "BERKLEY" and the "B" logo
are trademarks belonging to Berkley Publishing Corporation.

PRINTED IN THE UNITED STATES OF AMERICA

10   9   8   7   6   5   4   3   2   1

# ACKNOWLEDGMENTS

We are especially grateful to our editor at Doubleday, Les Pockell, and our agent, Jay Acton, for their help and encouragement.

We also thank our respective families for their support and understanding.

To my husband, FRANCIS JOSEPH DROHAN,
and my father,
JOHN MEREDITH SWACKHAMER

A.H.S.

To my mother, IRENE, and the memory of my father,
NAT

R.W.M.

This book is gratefully dedicated.

# ONE

## May

At 4 P.M. on a beautiful spring afternoon Clare Henson, the associate director of nursing, walked in the direction of the recovery room in Riverview's Astor Pavilion. The head nurse, Mary Green, had told her there was a gunshot wound in the unit and she wanted to hear the nurse's report before talking to the surgeon. In a corner of the break room she saw a private nurse with long auburn hair giving her report to the oncoming nurse. Clare recognized the woman facing her and nodded hello. When the private nurse turned around they both gasped.

"Clare!" the private nurse exclaimed, so loud that the other people in the room were startled.

"Karen Bovit!" Clare replied, more subdued.

Karen rushed over and hugged her. "God, what a surprise! This is incredible. How many years has it been?" They looked each other over. "It must be almost ten years. Amazing." Karen took Clare's hand. "God, I can't believe this is my old roommate. You look *terrific*, I mean it."

"You should have seen me a few years ago, Kar'," she said. "I was like a blimp."

"My God," Karen exclaimed. "So how'd you do it, chubby? I wish I knew your secret. I could lose a few." Karen's tone was full of affection. The other nurses in the room were all ears but trying to look busy.

"That's not true," Clare said, looking her up and down. "I can tell at a glance you still have a hyperactive metabolism."

"Sure," said Karen.

"I have to exercise constant, rigid self-control," said Clare. It was then that Karen noticed Clare's badge.

"So, I see you've got stripes now," said Karen, trying to sound nonchalant. "Associate director of nursing. Very impressive."

"It's a lot of hard work," said Clare.

"I thought we agreed in college we would never become administrators?" Karen teased.

"I'm still a working nurse, Karen," Clare said in a slightly defensive tone. "Now I get to nurse a whole hospital full of patients instead of just a few."

"And make more money," Karen said jokingly.

"Money has nothing to do with it," said Clare, laughing easily.

"Not bad, not bad at all." Karen was as surprised as she was impressed. Clare's tall, straight posture, the streak of gray, the "handsome" features—it was difficult for her to connect this clearly important person with the chubby kid she had roomed with in college.

"Listen, Karen, I'd really *love* to talk. But I've got a million things to do." She glanced at her clipboard list.

"And you must be busy. It seems so long since our student nursing days, doesn't it? We'll have to get together soon."

"How about meeting me after work today?" asked Karen quickly. Seeing Clare was so exciting. She often thought about her old college friends. She had lost touch with almost all of them, a situation which on occasion made her feel depressed.

Almost automatically, Clare replied, "Tonight's out." She knew her husband wouldn't appreciate being left with the kids. Karen pouted and Clare could tell that her refusal was being misinterpreted as the standoffishness of a "superior."

"Sure," said Karen. "Some other time." Both of them knew that their rediscovered relationship was in imminent danger.

"You know," said Clare, "on second thought, I'll just call home and tell Ken I'll be late," she said. "He'll complain, of course."

"That's great," said Karen.

Clare smiled. "It'll do me good to get out. And, by the way, why didn't I think of this before! Joan Fisher is working here at Riverview, or did you know that already?"

"Are you kidding me?" Karen exclaimed. "Hey, listen to me," she said, more subdued. "I'm starting to regress to my college days again! Even my voice is starting to sound like a kid's, and I haven't even had a drink! Joanie the Phony. Can you get ahold of her? I'd really love to see her too."

"That should be no problem," said Clare. "I see her every day practically, lucky me. In fact, she's my head nurse in the Surgical Intensive Care Unit on the afternoon shift. Today's her day off. I'll call her at home and see if she can join us at a place near here."

"Associate director . . . head nurse. I truly am impressed. Our alumnae have done well for themselves, haven't they?" Karen said.

"You're not exempting yourself, are you?" asked Clare.

"Not at all," said Karen. "I like private nursing. I'm independent, and I consider myself a good health care provider. I didn't sell out like you." She softened this with a big smile, to make sure Clare wouldn't be offended.

"Of course, you may be a *little* surprised by Joan," Clare said.

"How so?"

"I'll let you see for yourself," said Clare. "Okay, look, I've got work to do. Let's meet in the Astor lobby—do you know where that is?—at around 5 P.M. I'll call Joan and have her meet us there."

"God, I can't believe this!" said Karen once again. "What great luck to run into you. It'll be so great to have the three of us together again!"

Riverview Hospital sprawled along the eastern bank of the city's main waterway. From the highway that edged the river below, the hospital's massive stone foundations and Deco towers gave it the look of an ancient fortress. Yet few of those who worked at Riverview doubted that—despite its many problems—the hospital's medical care was state of the art. On the street, white uniforms predominated.

The lobby of the Astor Pavilion had once been the grand entrance of the entire hospital. When the new building was constructed, the Astor lobby became a kind of glorified employee hangout. In the center of its marble rotunda stood an incongruous breakfast-and-snack cart with its too cheerful yellow and white umbrella. Karen was sitting on a polished wooden bench near this umbrella, idly listening to an argument between two interns, when she felt a tap on her shoulder.

"This is unreal!" Joan Fisher cried out as Karen turned around. Joan gave her a big hug and babbled something

Karen didn't even hear. Her voice was suddenly thick with tears, and Karen, too, was very moved. Joan could drive you crazy with her incessant emotional roller-coaster ride. Yet her emotions were not only sincere, they were exciting. Suddenly being with her again, Karen wondered how she had lived without her all these years. How had she let such a wonderful friendship fall victim of inertia and laziness? Not that Clare was any less dear to her, but Joan was . . . well, still Joan. She had always been the crazy one of the three roommates, the most direct, the most intelligent, and also the most unstable.

"Jesus, look at you," said Joan with her New York accent. She held her friend out at arm's length. "Just as gorgeous as ever."

"And how about you? You haven't aged a bit," Karen said without much conviction. It wasn't really true, and they both knew it. Joan did look older. Naturally, they were *all* older by nearly a decade. Karen seemed hardly to have aged at all. And Clare had grown into her age so that it felt as if her youth had merely been a rather clumsy dress rehearsal. Joan, though, seemed a bit worse for the wear. She had never been great-looking. Karen thought her nose too prominent, her face a bit ferretlike. Yet, despite that, of the three, Joan had always been far and away the most popular and attractive to men.

There was one obvious explanation. She was sexually precocious and had come into college quite experienced, while both Karen and Clare had been virgins. There was something else as well—that mysterious quality known as sex appeal. Karen often wondered about it, and the three of them sometimes even discussed it. Karen was good-looking, so much so that men seemed afraid to approach her. Clare, in those days, was chubby and too uncomfortable with herself to be very sexy. Joan, however, was only really happy when she was with a man. Karen and Clare, in fact, hadn't known the half of it; although the three of them were roommates, Joan had successfully kept the details of her private life a secret. She had had many boyfriends, not all of them the kind you would take home to mother. Once she was delivered to the dorm at around 5 A.M. in a giant "semi" truck. She hopped out of the high vehicle and, as it roared away, staggered into the dorm room, mumbled "Wow" or some such thing, collapsed on the bed, and slept till the sun went down. Karen had disapproved and envied her at the same time.

Now Joan, at thirty-two, looked as if she had kept up this kind of life past the point where she could sustain it. Her hands, as Karen held them, seemed rough and uncared for, the too red nail polish chipping off. Her lipstick was slightly awry and had smudged her very white capped front teeth. Yet, despite this generally slovenly appearance, there was still something very attractive and alluring about Joan Fisher. And unless she had suddenly taken up the violin, a fresh hickey on the left side of her neck was evidence of her continuing activities.

"Ooh, I can't stand you," said Joan, "you look so damn neat and clean." She spoke with her characteristic slur— "lazy lips," the school's speech pathologist had called it. That was a charge, as they used to joke, that half the guys at college could easily refute. "You're preppy!" she exclaimed with real amazement, as if she had remembered a different Karen. "You're just like our dear old roomie and present-day boss."

"You don't know me very well," said Karen, but Joan ignored her.

"And here she comes now," Joan said sarcastically, "Wonder Woman." Clare was approaching them from down the corridor. "The white tornado," Joan added to herself.

Karen laughed, but uncomfortably. She remembered Joan's tendency toward divisiveness and wanted above all things to have a pleasant reunion. "She has prospered, hasn't she?" Karen said mildly.

"Kee-rist!" said Joan. "There's no stopping her. You wouldn't believe it."

"Karen," said Clare, bussing her cheek. "Joan." She took Joan's hand, and as an afterthought kissed her also. "Sorry I'm late. We had an emergency on Astor Four. A hemorrhage. One of our new girls—women," she corrected herself seamlessly, "didn't know how to handle it. Man almost bled to death. Oh well," she laughed, "all in a day's work. Well, we chose nursing!"

Karen nodded, professionally. Is this what we're going to talk about—great hemorrhages of our time? she wondered.

"Let's go to the Post Mortem for drinks," said Joan.

Clare said, "I won't be able to stay very long. I've got to get home. If you two want to have dinner, just go ahead without me." She smiled in a vulnerable way. "Ken needs me. He's all alone with the kids and had a really hard day," she added.

"Poor thing!" said Joan. "Not harder than trying to do nursing in this 650-bed madhouse." She looked over at Karen and raised her unplucked eyebrows, giving an ever so slight Mona Lisa smile. Karen was, of course, intrigued. She knew nothing about Clare's home situation but hoped to get the whole story from Joan before the evening was through.

The Post Mortem was a dark alley, lined on one side with a polished mahogany bar, on the other with tiny tables and incredibly uncomfortable wrought-iron chairs. Even in midweek it was packed with people, most of them doctors and nurses trying to unwind from the tension of the hospital. In the back, however, was a reasonable restaurant, with thick padded booths and a low ceiling. The three women settled themselves into one of the booths and ordered drinks. Karen had white wine, Clare her usual, Perrier with a twist. Joan had a double vodka on the rocks.

"So, Joan," Karen began, "the last I heard about you, you were married and going to medical school." She had heard this surprising tale from another private nurse at St. Barnabas, where she had been working.

"Jeez, that was years ago."

"Then I take it you're not married anymore," Karen said. Joan shook her head. "What happened?"

"What happened. Well, you asked for it. Now you're going to get the whole thing." She gulped her drink. "What happened was that I met Bob . . . Bob Miller . . . when he was a medical student, and we got married. We were married for two and a half years, when I—"

"Whoa, what's your hurry?" Karen said. "I don't want your résumé. I want all the gory details. You know, the girl talk."

Clare smiled uncomfortably. She had heard this all before, even lived through much of it with Joan. She didn't feel like hearing it again.

"Girl talk . . . girl talk. Well, Bob was sweet," Joan said. "Clare knows him." She nodded noncommittally. "He was, uh, going to make an honest woman of me, isn't that right, Clare?"

"Fat chance," said Clare with rather surprising vehemence. It didn't come out as humorously as she intended.

"I'll ignore that," said Joan, and they all laughed a little too loudly.

"And so we got married. It was really pretty nice. His folks sent us to Europe for the honeymoon. Don't worry, they could afford it. Where was I? Robert. We got an apartment in one of those high-priced, high-rise filing cabinets. And we were pretty happy together. No, to be honest, we were *very* happy together, more happy, I guess, than I've ever been with a guy. And that's saying something."

She paused to drink, then seemingly forgot to pick up the story again.

"So?" Karen said finally.

"Well, it's a bit difficult to explain. Not to mention painful. But being with Bob all the time, and with his stupid friends, made my whole brilliant nursing career"—she glanced nervously at Clare—"seem a bit dubious."

Karen pondered this "Joan-ism." "What's that supposed to mean? He looked down on you?" she asked finally.

"Naw," Joan drawled. "Not exactly. But when I compared the way doctors and nurses got treated . . . no, that's not it either." She paused. "You see, when you're married to someone, after a while you start to see yourself through their eyes. And I didn't like what I saw. I mean, nurses have some pretty menial tasks when you think about it. There's nothing very glorious about emptying bedpans, is there? Nothing very intellectually stimulating about giving some sick old man an enema at three o'clock in the morning. As Bob used to say, a nurse is really nothing but a glorified maid, in just a slightly different uniform."

"Sounds like a charmer," said Karen under her breath.

"In other words, you lost your sense of purpose," Clare interrupted. She was growing impatient with Joan's monologue.

"I guess so," said Joan, unconvinced. "When you come right down to it, I couldn't stand the pettiness of being a nurse anymore. Bob had started his residency at a city hospital. So he suggested I quit. I think he was embarrassed being married to a nurse. I couldn't see myself just loafing around like a housewife. I thought I'd just get . . . into trouble." She gave a mischievous smile, and, knowing Joan, they all laughed. "You see, I know it sounds corny, but what I really wanted was respect." The words came out passionately and unrehearsed now. "You remember, I was pretty smart in college, in fact I'd say smarter than most of the premeds." Karen nodded. It was true: Joan had in fact been brilliant when she chose to apply herself.

"We were always very proud of you," said Clare evenly. She sounded as if she were talking to one of her kids.

"So why should they walk away with all the glory, not to mention all the money?"

"Who are 'they'?" Clare asked a bit sophomorically, but Joan just ignored her.

"So I decided that if I couldn't beat 'em I would join 'em. The medical school here had a program for overaged underachievers like myself, and so I applied and got in." She had been fidgeting with an empty glass and was relieved when a fresh vodka almost magically appeared. Joan laughed, but without humor. "And that's when the fun began. Medical school wasn't intrinsically hard, but you had to have cooperation. And it turned out that Bob didn't really want competition in the doctor department from his little woman, despite what he said."

Karen watched her take a long swallow of her second drink and wondered if there was more to it than that.

"C'mon, Joan," Clare said, bristling. "You're rationalizing. You forget that I was there, at least for the second half of this business, and . . ."

" 'S really true," said Joan with her lazy-lipped slur. "Everything became real shitty after that. Look, Karen, do I have to spell it all out for you? I mean, our social life went to pot, our sex life went to pot."

"I thought that's where it started," Clare said dryly.

"Pot," she added, by way of explanation when neither of them laughed.

Joan mercifully ignored her. "Try getting romantic when you're both working twelve-, fourteen-hour shifts, *different* shifts, I might add. When my husband was horny I was collapsing in my clothes onto the sofa, and vice versa. You get the picture."

"We've all worked shifts," Clare said unsympathetically.

"And he was a perfect Neanderthal underneath when it came to the male ego trip. He did everything he could to make life difficult for me." Sensing the skepticism on Clare's face, she said, "Not that I *couldn't* have done it if I'd really wanted to." Her voice was getting whisky-loud. "I could have. And I know you probably think I'm a coward and a weakling," she addressed Clare, "but in the end I guess I didn't really care about it enough. I mean, I discovered that you have to really want to be a doctor. I was doing it for all the wrong reasons when all I wanted, I guess, was to be a different kind of nurse. Am I making any sense?"

"Perfect sense," Karen said enthusiastically. "I've had exactly the same kind of thoughts."

"We all have," said Clare.

"You see, it's precisely because of that that I became a private nurse," Karen said. "I got tired of being treated like part of the furniture, instead of someone first-rate in her own right. I mean, a nurse is *different* than a doctor, does different things. Not better, not worse."

"In my opinion," said Clare a bit formally, "nurses are just as important as doctors. It's the human touch. Not too many doctors have it. The doctors diagnose and treat diseases," she added, "but nurses diagnose and treat human feelings. It's such a different focus. . . ."

"So what happened?" Karen turned back to Joan. "Did

you flunk out of medical school? I mean, you're back in nursing, right? Was that by default?''

"Not really," said Joan. "Nobody flunks out of medical school. If you want to stay in, they keep you. I just couldn't stand the environment. So I came back to nursing, with a focus on science, mainly thanks to Clare here." She lifted her glass in her friend's direction. "I needed a job and I'd heard that Clare was a honcho over here at Riverview. I called her and they hired me that week. And I've been here ever since. Four years now. I went into the one area that was the most high-tech. Surgical intensive care. So I get to play Buck Rogers with the glory boys now, to fool around with the hardware, all the latest stuff. If I wasn't so old I'd probably go back to school and get a Ph.D. in something.''

"Maybe nursing administration?" Clare asked, interested.

"Oh, sure," Joan drawled. "Maybe electrical engineering. I'd like to learn to design those gadgets we use in the ICU. Anything where I won't be bothered by a bunch of whining, ungrateful patients anymore. Actually, I don't know why I'm complaining. In our unit we ship 'em out as soon as they utter two coherent sounds in a row.''

"Don't you get any pleasure from helping people?" Karen asked, surprised. With the gentle help of the white wine, she was being agreeably scandalized by Joan's brash, cynical personality.

"Not really," said Joan. "What interests me in nursing now is the intellectual stimulation. The Problem of the Patient, not the *problems* of the patient."

"Clever," said Clare. "I'll have to remember that."

Joan acknowledged the compliment, although Karen was sure that she had read the line somewhere.

"Joan was in a pretty bad way," Clare explained to Karen, "but I knew she would be an outstanding nurse, and she is, despite what she says. The funny thing is, Joan, you're actually *great* with patients," Clare said.

"Oh, bullshit," said Joan.

"She's right about one thing: her forte is in the intellectual side of nursing. We don't have another nurse who understands high-tech stuff better than Joan."

"I have found my niche," Joan announced. Typically, she didn't seem entirely happy with that situation.

"And what happened to Bob?" Karen asked.

"Oh, Bob," Joan said, exchanging a knowing look with Clare. "Well, as soon as I came here Robert decided that he had to follow me." She lit up one of her high-tar cigarettes and offered the pack around. To Karen's surprise, Clare took one. "Men are crazy, aren't they? I mean, there must be a dozen hospitals in this city, not to mention that vast wasteland outside the city, and Robert Miller just 'had to' choose my hospital."

"Let's be fair," said Clare, exhaling with sensual pleasure. She was a "social smoker." "Riverview *does* have one of the outstanding orthopedic departments in the country."

"And would you believe that he still comes off like Big Daddy whenever he sees me," Joan said vehemently. "God, you know I really hate that. Meets me in the hallway, starts lecturing me about my language and uniforms. One time he even tried to grab me right there among the patients to give me a shake for some misbehavior or another."

Karen laughed helplessly. Joan hadn't lost her talent for self-dramatization. Even Clare, Perrier-sober, was amused by Joan's verbal antics.

"I believe you, I do." Clare paused. "You know," she said uncertainly, "he once made eyes at me."

The two other women looked at her, shocked.

"Oh, now you *are* kidding me," Joan drawled.

"It's true," said Clare. "After that disastrous time when we went out to lunch with him at the diner." She turned to Karen. "I went with the two of them to that place on the corner, to try and patch things up." She smiled. "I did such a good job that Joan wound up throwing a dish of rice pudding at Bob's head! Luckily, she missed."

"I hit the curtains, though, remember," Joan said happily, "and wound up having to pay the owners twenty-five dollars. I haven't been too welcome at the Plaka since then."

"Did he really come on to you? What'd he do? What'd he say?" asked Karen, amazed. "I have to meet this guy. He must have some nerve," she added.

"I never got close enough to find out," Clare said. "He said"—she was actually blushing now—"well, it wasn't so much *what* he said as how he . . ."

"Oh, c'mon, c'mon," Karen said eagerly. "Out with it. We've got to know." Deep down, she was happy and grateful that the conversation had really taken off and the three of them had found a little door into their schoolgirl past. For a brief moment, they could have been back in room 309 of their dorm.

"Well, he wasn't very direct," Clare said. She reached over for another one of Joan's cigarettes.

"Here you are, you moocher," said Joan without malice. "Keep the whole pack."

Clare waved her away but deftly shook out a single cigarette, lit it up, and blew out the match. "He said a lot of things. He implied that he had been attracted to me from the first. He also said that in some essential way, because I was a mother, I reminded him of his own mother . . ."

"That's Bob," said Joan, disgusted.

"Is that a non sequitur or what?" asked Karen.

"Not for Bob," Joan replied vehemently. "He invented Freud."

"Isn't that a beautiful thought, though?" asked Clare. Karen had the feeling she had replayed this scene over and over in her mind and had it all down by heart.

"I could care less what he does," Joan said. In spite of Joan's apparent detachment, Karen felt that she might still have some mixed feelings about her ex-husband.

"Well, Joan," Clare said, deliberately trying to bait her, "you gave him up, didn't you? A handsome man like that, too. So naturally you wouldn't care, right?"

"Tell me," said Karen, "would you, you know, have you . . ." She trod gently. Marriage was unknown territory, and so in a sense was the new Clare.

Clare exhaled smoke through her nostrils. "Karen, I'm a married woman, with two children." She was being deliberately sphinxlike. Karen enjoyed the game.

"Therefore you don't have the normal urges anymore? You don't get excited when a handsome stranger looks at you in *that* way and tells you he finds you attractive? In other words, it's all quiet on the suburban front."

Joan, misunderstanding Karen's irony, said, "Bullshit!"

"I love my husband," said Clare in a poorly constructed evasion.

Joan took one of her own cigarettes off the table and said to Clare, with complete inconsistency, "You shouldn't smoke these—you a nurse!" She then lit up. As always, she was clumsy but cute. Although her lungs were probably coal black from fifteen years of tobacco, she still puffed like a schoolgirl. Her voice was getting a bit loud and abrasive, yet Karen felt a warm, almost maternal affection for her friend at that moment.

"What's marriage like, Clare?" Karen asked thoughtfully.

Joan didn't want to talk about marriage anymore. She was examining the fascinating insides of a cigarette filter.

"Marriage? I take it, then, that you're still not married."

"No." She paused. "I saw someone for years and years," she said vaguely. "We broke it off about six months ago. *He* was married. I don't suppose that would qualify." She hesitated to talk about the affair. "Lately, though, I've become sort of fascinated with women our age who have real families, you know, with noisy kids all over the place."

"That's just some kind of menstrual or hormonal activity," said Joan. "It'll pass."

"I suppose so. The whole topic has become my new obsession since I passed thirty." She turned to Clare. "So tell me about it, and about your kids. Did they turn out nice? What a question, huh? How old are they now?"

"Becky is ten and a half, and Kenny is nine."

"Nice ages," said Karen. "I've got a niece who's ten and a half."

"Actually, I think they're terrible ages," said Clare. "Mischievous as hell, especially Kenny. And, while we're being perfectly honest, a year and a half between kids is simply too little time. Both in diapers at the same time, both going off to school within a year of each other. And both will be in college at the same time. There's a frightening thought! And the jealousy, the rivalry! It's unbelievable."

"I never thought of that," said Karen. But she could not be so easily deterred from her dreams of having a houseful of little Karens. "It seems like such an awful responsibility," she said, finishing her own thought aloud.

"I can barely get *myself* together every day," Joan piped up, "never mind taking care of a couple of rug rats. Why'd you have 'em so close together, anyway?"

"Rug rats," said Clare, chuckling. "Well, it wasn't exactly planned that way, if you know what I mean. But I don't regret it. They do make the struggle all worthwhile, I think. Any prospects for you on the horizon, Karen?''

"Not at the moment," said Karen. "You have to be so sure before you get married. I'm sorry I waited this long, because I think you get more discriminating as you get older.''

Clare gave her a probing stare. "Maybe I can introduce you to some men here at Riverview. It's clear you've changed your mind about marriage." She hadn't forgotten how Joan and Karen had tried to talk her out of marrying just after graduation.

"Marriage is bullshit," Joan mumbled. Their resident cynic had spoken the final word. She rested her chin on her bunched fists.

Clare just raised her eyebrows and continued. "Well, I won't say that it's been easy for me and Ken. He's had his share of problems." She stopped. "Well, that sounds terrible—like God knows what! What I mean is, he's had job problems, and money worries can really sap a person's energy. When we started out together, after graduation, we both had equivalent jobs. R.N. and junior engineer are pretty equivalent.''

"Junior engineer!" said Joan. "How cute!"

"That's what it's called, Joan," said Clare, not smiling. "As time went by, though, I kept getting these promotions while Ken—well, he just didn't. He made it to foreman and then stopped.''

"What's the next stop?"

"Superintendent. Then possibly vice-president. It was the same old story. The boss's son-in-law got the jobs.''

"Foreman's not bad, is it?" asked Karen.

"Well, it's like everything else." She shrugged her shoulders. "You gotta keep moving up or you stagnate.''
Karen suspected this was Clare's philosophy, not necessar-

ily Ken's. "And to make matters worse, the housing industry has its ups and downs all the time. He gets laid off periodically. That's really pretty hard on him, on us. It seems to be getting a little better, now that interest rates are coming down again. But it hasn't been easy."

"I'd like to meet your family," Karen said. "I bet Ken's changed from that lanky kid . . ."

"Still lanky," said Clare, laughing. "A little bald on the top. But still adorable." She sounded as if she meant it. "I'm sure he'd like to see you too. Maybe you could come up to see us, if you don't mind traveling. It's hard for us to get into the city. Baby-sitter problems."

"You know," Joan said, tuning in on the conversation suddenly, "that's exactly what a nurse is expected to be nowadays, a baby-sitter. And, by the way, I wouldn't exclude the private-duty variety from that description."

Karen, although aware that Joan was drinking a lot, was unable to bite back her retort. "Look, Joan, speak for yourself! You know, when we were in school you set out to be a real nurse. If I remember correctly, we took a pledge to do that. If you now find that you're twirling dials and pushing buttons all day, it's your own fault. Real nurses practice their profession, Joan. Nobody's forcing you to be an employee of some hospital corporation."

"I don't go for this crap about the *real* nursing experience," Joan responded. "You know, since you got here, Karen, all you've done is sound like a commercial for the goddamned American Nursing Association."

"That makes me feel just great, Joan," Karen said, forcing herself to remain calm. The girl was irrational! She suddenly remembered how annoying Joan could be. "I think what you need is a cup of coffee. Black."

"Is that your bitchy way of telling me I'm too drunk to argue with?"

"Joan!" Clare said, scandalized. "Control yourself! That's Karen you're talking to!"

"Oh, hell," she said, "I can talk to Karen however I like. She's one person I don't need to be phony with."

"Phony Joanie," Karen said, and they all laughed, tensely. That had been their nickname for her in college, because of her chameleonlike transformation around men.

"Hey, girls," Joan said in a stage whisper, "isn't that Phil Mackey over there?" She had quickly forgotten the whole argument.

Dr. Philip Mackey had emerged from the swirling smoke of the Post Mortem bar and was surveying the restaurant area for fresh conquests. He was a short man in his late fifties, with a neatly trimmed white mustache. He spied the three nurses and made his way toward them, weaving between the closely spaced tables.

"Dr. Mackey, my favorite anesthesiologist," Clare said with political suavity.

"And Ms. Henson, my favorite nursing administrator," he said, "and fellow bored board member." He had his eyes on Joan, however.

"Dr. Mackey," Clare said, "this is Karen Bovit. She is a private nurse who will be working with us . . ."

"Happy to make your acquaintance," he said, nodding his head and smiling. He was the kind of man who could make a menu sound sexually suggestive. She smiled politely. "Well, I'm glad to see you're making yourself at home at Riverview, Karen. And you've discovered the most important part of any hospital, the watering hole. You've already made friends with the two nicest nurses in the hospital."

"College roommates," Clare offered.

He turned toward Joan. "And Ms. Fisher. The pride of the Intensive Care. So, where have you been hiding yourself, little girl?" He leaned over, took her hand, and kissed her on the mouth. Karen was surprised at the kiss—it seemed longer and wetter than necessary under the circumstances.

"I'm going to the bar. Can I bring you ladies anything?"

"Vodka on the rocks for me," said Joan swiftly. "A double."

Karen and Clare exchanged glances. Clare said, "Thanks, but no thanks," and Karen shook her head. While Mackey was in the other room, struggling for the bartender's attention, Karen blurted out, "This was great! We should really try to stay in touch from now on. I can't believe we could have drifted so far apart."

"It's easy to say, 'Let's get together,'" said Joan, "but we won't. Clare—tell Karen how many times we've had drinks together." She made a zero sign with her fingers.

Clare ignored her. "You're right, Karen. It was great catching up. Next time maybe we can talk about old times."

"Okay, now let's talk about old men," said Joan. "Isn't Phil Mackey the best-dressed doctor in the hospital?"

Karen, still filled with the emotion of the moment, ignored her. "Let's have lunch next week. How about Wednesday?"

Clare said, "That sounds great." She took out her appointment book and made an entry. They both looked at Joan, but she was already absorbed in Dr. Mackey's return. Clare said quietly, "I'll invite her tomorrow, Karen."

"I understand you were a hero this morning, Doctor," Joan said a little too loudly. Mackey beamed with pride and handed Joan her drink.

"Well, I'm glad you see it that way. The surgeon can't make a move without me. I might as well get some credit after getting woken up at that ungodly hour!" Joan turned to chat animatedly with the doctor, ignoring her two friends.

"The transformation of Joan," Clare whispered to Karen. "She becomes a different person around men."

"And always did," said Karen, laughing. "That's our Joanie." Even Joan's face had undergone an instantaneous face lift. Before, there had been a noticeable sag to it, with a downturned mouth. Now, talking to Dr. Mackey, she positively glowed. "I can't say I like her better this way," Karen whispered, "but you've got to admit she's a lot better-looking."

When Mackey sat down, however, the mood changed. Clare looked at her watch. "Oh, dear, it's almost seven o'clock. I'd better get out of here or I'll miss my train. I've got to go home and take care of my 'rug rats.'" She shot a glance at Joan. "Enjoy yourself."

"Wait up!" said Karen, looking at her watch. "Are you calling a cab?"

"What about having dinner, Kar'?" Joan asked at the last minute. "They've got terrific food here, really."

Mackey looked pleased but politely asked, "You're not leaving, are you?"

"I'm not very hungry," said Karen, which was a lie. "I think I'll go home. It's been a long hard day. I'm done in."

"You and me both," said Mackey.

"Okay, Karen," said Joan, kissing her sloppily as she rose to go. "Call me tomorrow, won't you? And, hey, I'm sorry that we argued before."

"From you, Joan, I will consider that an abject apology," said Karen. "Wait for me, Clare. I'll go along with you for a few blocks."

"You mean I get to have the great Dr. Mackey all to myself?" said Joan in the little girl voice she sometimes affected. "Oh, lucky, lucky me." Karen groaned out loud at this sudden corniness, and Mackey laughed in a good-natured way.

"And what about you, Joan, are you coming?" Clare asked.

Joan leered up at them. "Not yet, I'm not. I think I'll stick around here for a while. Dr. Mackey here has just invited me to go dining and dancing with him," she said. "Isn't that right, Dr. Mackey?"

"Phil," he corrected her.

"Well then, Phil, fill 'er up." She jiggled her empty glass at his face. "Phil tells me he's a regular disco duck. Do you think I should believe him? You know, I'd like to go to Roseland. Anyone for Roseland? I've never gone ballroom dancing. That would be a trip. But I think this guy's too old for me, don't you, Clare? They'll take him for my father, even my grandfather. Grandpa Mackey. He's gonna get busted on a morals charge."

"Now who's getting Freudian?" asked Karen.

Joan laughed and placed her palm on Mackey's designer shirt. Karen whispered something to Clare, and they laughed.

"Watch yourself, Clare," said Mackey menacingly. "Anything you say can be used against you at the next board meeting."

"In that case, I'll do the smart thing and say nothing. Nice seeing you, Dr. Mackey," she said amiably. "Joan, take care of yourself. I'll see you tomorrow. Behave yourself!" Her concern showed through the banter.

"Are you kidding? This is going to be a purely educational experience. Phil intends to teach me all the latest advances in anesthesiology," said Joan.

"Which is her way of saying," he confided to Karen, "that she thinks I'm going to put her to sleep."

"Where can I drop you?" asked Clare as the warm spring breeze gusted in their faces.

"My apartment is about ten bocks from here. It's a nice evening. I think I'll just walk."

"Are you sure?" asked Clare. "Is it safe?"

They walked up to the corner of the avenue. "Well, she hasn't changed much, has she?" Karen declared. "Oh, lucky, lucky me," she said, imitating Joan quite effectively. "She's got to be kidding!"

"I think she is," said Clare dryly. "At least, I hope she is."

"And that Mackey! What a sleaze!"

"Karen!" said Clare. "I have to work with him on the hospital board. Besides, he's not such a bad guy once you get to know him. I admit he doesn't make the best first impression."

"Why does she throw herself at a man like that?" Karen asked, not expecting an answer. "Doesn't she read the newspapers? She's likely to come down with some dreadful disease."

An empty cab pulled up at the curb. "You're a dear," said Clare, squeezing her hand. "Come on, let me drop you at your apartment. That way we can talk some more."

They chatted freely on the way downtown. Karen was feeling good when she hopped out of the taxi in front of her apartment house. She gaily waved good-bye to Clare, whose cab screeched as it pulled away from the curb. Humming to herself, she greeted the doorman, got the mail, and let herself into her apartment. All in all, it had been a really interesting day—just the break she needed from the rut she had been in at St. Barnabas.

She went into the bathroom, took off her clothes, showered, and put on a pair of "friendly" flannel pajamas. Then she got a big hunk of cold steak from the refrigerator, cut it into slices, poured ketchup on the side, and took it into bed with her. After devouring this, she pulled her big, outrageously expensive down comforter up to her chin, took a best-selling paperback novel from the night table, and tried to read. In five minutes she was drowsy and shut off the light.

Since breaking up with Mike six months before there had been hardly a night she hadn't gone to sleep at least vaguely depressed. She would force herself to think about her childhood, about some happy event like a birthday party or the times when the family went on picnics before her mother died. Then she would fall asleep, her dreams gently launched from these memories. Right now, however, she was not depressed. She had started in a new hospital, with an interesting case and new people. And most important, without any warning she had her two best college friends restored to her.

As she reflected on the events she realized that over the years hardly a month had gone by that she hadn't thought, in some little way, about these friends. Often it was something inconsequential that reminded her of one or another of them—a Simon and Garfunkel song she had first heard with Joan, the expensive English hairbrush that Clare had used and she had envied.

It was strange. On the surface at least they were so different—and the years had only accentuated those differences. Yet in the ten years that had gone by she had never made such friends again.

Clare arrived home late that evening. She stooped down and removed her son's skateboard from the path. The lawn was beginning to grow, and she made a mental note to take care of it that weekend.

"Hi, I'm home," she called. She was exhausted but exhilarated by the day's events.

"Upstairs," came her husband's voice. She put her

briefcase in their small office and hung up her light coat on the rack in the hallway. She had secretly hoped that the kids would be asleep by the time she arrived.

"Mommy!" Ken and Becky cried. She kissed each of them. "Where were you?" they asked.

"Did you have a good time?" asked her husband, Ken. He was a thin man, fit from outdoor work in his construction job and from his addiction to jogging. She gave him a kiss.

"What a day!" she said. "I'd like to talk," she added under her breath. "Let's get the show on the road."

"Oh, Mommy," said Becky, "Daddy was just telling us another story about boar hunting."

Clare disapproved of Ken's outrageous tall tales. "Tomorrow, pumpkin," said Clare. They got the kids quiet and put out the lights.

"So how'd it go? How did Karen look? Joan I won't even ask about."

"Don't be nasty," said Clare, kicking off her shoes under the kitchen table. "Karen looks great. Still not married," she added, a bit gossipy.

"How come?" he asked.

"Who knows? Her explanation sounded unconvincing. I do know this: she was seeing a married man for years. They broke it off some months ago."

"Sounds interesting," said Ken, laughing. "Well, you'll have to invite her up. I'd like to see her again."

"Don't get any ideas," said Clare, feigning jealousy. "There's some spaghetti on the stove."

"I'll have some later. Now I've some big news for you. David Morgan is in the hospital with chest pains."

"David Morgan?" he asked, going to the refrigerator for a light beer.

"Charlotte's husband!" Clare exclaimed impatiently. The importance of this event was self-explanatory to her.

"I'm sorry to hear about it," said Ken. "Your boss's husband's health is always paramount in my mind."

"Don't you remember?" said Clare. "Charlotte said that if David had another heart attack she was going to consider resigning."

"I'm beginning to understand," said Ken, smiling. "Still, it seems ghoulish of you to hope he has a heart attack," he teased.

"I didn't give him the heart condition," said Clare.

"Well, don't hold your breath," said Ken. He thought of his own job. "Maybe Charlotte has a daughter who wants the job. Or a niece. Or a dog."

Clare laughed. "Well, thanks for the compliment. I want that job and I'm going to get it."

"And you always get what you want," Ken said. "You got me, didn't you?" Behind these joking words, however, Clare sensed a discordant note of jealousy.

At 7 A.M., a few days later, Karen sat musing in the nurses' station. So much had happened, so quickly. Not only had she found Clare and Joan again but her new case, and this new hospital, promised to be challenging.

The call that woke her up earlier that week was from Dr. Ed Berg, a surgeon she often worked with at St. Barnabas. He asked her to come to Riverview and work with a young man who had been shot downtown during the night. Eric Sadler was the son of old friends who happened to be out of the country. Luckily, Karen was free at the moment. She quickly agreed to come in and had arrived at the hospital just before sunrise. She found Dr. Berg in the recovery room just before the operation. He was very abrupt, because the wound was so serious. Eric's chances, he confided, were no better than fifty-fifty. Yet thanks to Dr. Berg's good surgical technique, and his patient's youthful vigor, Eric Sadler had survived.

While waiting in the recovery room for the patient to come out of surgery, as Dr. Berg had requested, Karen looked around. The recovery room had about thirty beds along the walls. There was no one at the desk, except a young doctor who stood nearby. "Could you tell me who's the head nurse here?" Karen asked.

"Mary Green," said the doctor, smiling. "Over there by bed twelve." Mary had her back turned, talking to a patient. Karen walked over and waited for her to finish, and, when she turned, introduced herself. Mary's pale face remained impassive. She was an older woman with white hair and an erect posture.

"Have you registered at the nursing office yet?" was her only response.

Momentarily thrown off guard, Karen said, "No, I haven't registered yet. Dr. Berg wanted me to wait here."

"You should register first," said Mary Green. "You are not allowed in the recovery room until you are properly registered."

"I'm sorry, but while I have your attention, I would like to know, do I report directly to you, or is a staff nurse assigned to the case?"

"Riverview Hospital policy is that the private-duty nurses only function as companions to the patients in the recovery room. If they feel the need for a companion in this unit that's their business." She turned her back.

"You're right, it is," Karen said, barely able to mask her annoyance.

As Karen turned to leave, Mary continued. "Just a word of advice. Don't comment to anyone on the status of the patient. We don't want any false hopes raised."

" 'We' meaning 'real nurses,' I suppose," said Karen, laughing to cover her growing annoyance. "You know, I'm not stupid. I'm a professional nurse in private practice. I've been a nurse for over ten years. I made a *choice* to work for the patients rather than hospitals."

Mary Green's face colored. "Just who do you think you are?"

"Look," said Karen calmly, "I'm going to register at the nursing office. Forgive me for the lecture. You respect me and I'll respect you."

Mary nodded coldly.

As Karen walked out of the recovery room a young nurse approached her and said, "Welcome to Riverview! That was great! Mary Green's not used to staff nurses talking to her like that."

"Thanks," she said. "But that's not the reputation I'm looking for."

"Let me take you to the nursing office," said the young nurse. "By the way, I'm Jill Curtis. Where do you usually work?" she asked as they walked.

"St. Barnabas."

"How did you wind up here?" Jill asked.

"Dr. Berg asked me for a favor," said Karen. "We've worked together at St. Barnabas."

"Dr. Berg's a good guy. Well, here's the office," Jill said. "Hey, how about a cup of coffee?"

"I'd love some," said Karen. "I ran out this morning without a bite. Just give me a minute to take care of this paperwork."

In the nurses' lounge Jill introduced Karen around to the other nurses and poured a cup. They all talked shop for a while.

After the other nurses left, Karen had said to Jill, "I hate waiting." She paced up and down and watched the river traffic. It was four hours before Ed Berg had emerged from the operating room. His gown was covered with blood. Karen took one look at his exhausted yet excited face and knew Eric was going to be all right. . . .

"You must be a fellow insomniac," a man's voice said, startling her out of her reveries. "I didn't expect to see you here so early." Ed Berg was dressed in greens, his mask flopping down around his neck.

"You keep waking me up, Ed," she said, laughing. "I figured there was no point in trying to sleep anymore."

"Well, I'm glad you're here. I came in to talk to Eric before I start surgery for the day. I think it would be a great idea if you were there when I did so, Karen. He may not like the news I have to tell him." They walked to Eric's room from the nurses' station together.

"Well, Eric, how are you feeling?" asked Berg, sitting on his patient's bed. Eric was reading a sports magazine Karen had brought him.

"My throat's still sore from that tube they put down it," Eric said, yawning.

"Well, that will get better soon. Would you like some fruit ice? Karen, could you see that he gets some?" She nodded.

"Otherwise, I guess I'm okay," said Eric. "Still queasy from all these drugs. By the way, my parents called yesterday. They'll be here tomorrow. Am I really going to be okay, Dr. Berg?"

"Absolutely," said Berg. "You're a very lucky young man. I don't have to tell you all the things that *could* have happened to you from this gunshot."

"But I'm okay, right? Completely okay?" Eric asked anxiously. Berg glanced at Karen briefly. "What happened? Did they catch the guy who shot me?"

"They arraigned him yesterday, Eric," said Karen. "It was awfully brave of you to intervene the way you did. I'm cutting out all the articles in the papers for you. You made page three of the *Post*."

He laughed. "I don't care about that kind of junk," he said, but Karen could tell he was proud. "I'm not a hero, really. I was passing on the bus when I saw this guy choking a woman on the street. So I hopped off and tried to stop him. It was crazy. The opposite of what I thought I would do . . . but when you're in a situation like that . . ." His voice trailed off. "I'm short of breath," he gasped.

"That's normal," said Berg. "You need plenty of rest and tender loving care." There was a pause. "Listen, Eric, there is just one thing."

"Yeah?" he said nervously.

"You do have a colostomy, Eric. We're nearly positive it's temporary. We should have it reversed in a few months, when your intestines have had a chance to completely heal."

"Whoa," said Eric, brushing back his sandy-colored hair. "Run that by me one more time." His already pale face had gone white.

"It's a temporary opening in your abdomen. Don't look so shocked, Eric. It's standard operating procedure."

"You don't have to tell *me* what a colostomy is," he said, a bit annoyed. "I worked at the VA hospital last summer. I saw enough of them." He closed his eyes, fighting back tears.

"Then you know there are two kinds of colostomy," said Berg quickly. He glanced at his diver's watch. "Permanent and temporary. You've got the latter kind." He stood up. "Time to go."

Eric opened his eyes. "You said you're *almost* positive

it's temporary, Doctor," he said accusingly. "That doesn't sound so black and white."

Berg laughed. "You're a sharp kid, Eric."

"Besides, I'm not a kid," said Eric. "I'm eighteen years old already. I'm a high school graduate, or at least I will be if I can get out of here. So please don't talk down to me, Dr. Berg. I'm old enough to be told the truth."

"Eric, I've known you since you were little, and I've always been straight with you. I am telling you all the facts. The chances are ninety-nine out of a hundred that it's temporary. Okay? Look, I've got to run now. If you have any questions, just ask Karen here. She's here to help you."

When Berg had gone, Eric was silent. He almost seemed to resent Karen's presence, as if she were the doctor's co-conspirator against him.

"Temporary, huh?" he said, running his hand over his abdomen. "Do you think they could have it reversed by next month? Graduation's on the twentieth."

Karen knew it was very unlikely. She hesitated, and then decided that honesty was the best policy. "I doubt it," she said. "We can check with the doctor about it. You could attend the graduation anyway. Who'll know that you've got a temporary problem?"

He seemed to find this funny. "I'll be the hit of the prom, won't I? Dancing cheek to cheek . . . and bag to bag. What a turn-on."

"If somebody really likes you," said Karen in an older-sister voice, "it's not going to matter to them that you have this."

"You obviously don't know teenage girls," said Eric, trying to sound cynical. Actually he was encouraged by her words.

"How old do you think I am?" she laughed. "No, don't

answer that. In any case, it wasn't that long ago that I was in school myself."

He smiled, embarrassed. "I didn't mean it that way." He blushed.

Karen sat down next to the bed and stared at him. "You know, Eric," she said, "I'm really glad I took this case. Knowing you makes me feel good."

"Boy, are you sentimental!" he said, covering up his own emotions.

This is like having the younger brother I always wanted, she thought.

"You obviously don't know what girls are like nowadays."

"Maybe I'm out of touch," she admitted. "I know *I* wouldn't care."

"You mean that?" he asked. He stared at her. "I guess you do. Hey, why do you come in so early in the morning? I thought you didn't start till eight."

"I just like to see how you're doing," she said evasively. "You're not here just eight hours a day, are you?"

"I guess not," he said, staring at her. "You know, I like you, Karen," he said finally.

"I like you too," she said.

"Sure," he said. "But not the way I like you." He stared into her eyes. "Hey," he said suddenly, breaking the mood, "do you think we could go for a walk or something? I've got to get rid of this thing before graduation."

"Let's walk to the nurses' station," said Karen. She knew it was good for surgical patients to ambulate as soon as possible. She helped him up out of the bed and draped his robe over his shoulders. Eric linked his arm through hers and slowly began inching his way out the door. The hallway was empty, except for a lone old woman pushing her IV pole down the corridor.

"Come on, Eric. Let's race her!" said Karen.

"Oh, give me a break. I can barely talk and chew gum at the same time."

"Only kidding," said Karen, "Just concentrate on your breathing and try to relax. Don't worry if your insides hurt. That's normal." The two walked together slowly and silently. They were about halfway to the nurses' station when, from behind them, a man's voice boomed, "Where's the medication nurse?"

Wincing inwardly, Karen said, "Steady, Eric. Just concentrate on your breathing."

Dr. Philip Mackey rushed by them and confronted the nurse who was sitting at the desk. "Get me 10 mg. of IV Valium STAT," he sputtered. "I'll give it myself, since none of you nurses seem to have the time to do it!"

Ellen Garrison rose to her feet, holding a chart in both hands. Her normally soft gray eyes were flashing fire. "Dr. Mackey," she said, "if you're talking about Mavis Brown . . ."

"Of course I'm talking about Mavis Brown, and she's supposed to be in the operating room now, but nobody has given her her pre-op medicine. So get me the Valium and I'll give it myself." He shook his head in disgust.

Ellen opened the chart, pointing to the latest entry in the nurses' notes. She said calmly, "If you had bothered to read my note you would know that I have been paging you for the past half hour. I wanted to inform you that Mavis has had an allergic reaction to Valium at the dentist. Therefore, I withheld the medication and charted my reasons."

"I interviewed Mavis just last night. The woman doesn't *have* any allergies. You must be wrong. Maybe she's allergic to her dentist's cologne or something."

Ellen was about to lose her patience. She clenched her teeth. "Doctor, I'm not going to beg you to do your job.

Read my note. She states clearly she forgot to tell the doctor about her reaction.''

Mackey's face reddened with anger. "And I don't like your attitude. Don't think this smugness is going to go unreported to Charlotte Morgan.''

Karen and Eric had reached the nurses' station. "What a lowlife," said Eric under his breath. Karen registered no reaction but steered him around, back toward the room.

"Joan, that doctor you were with the other night is a real loser!" said Karen. "You know, he almost gave IV Valium to a woman who was allergic!"

It was a rainy afternoon, and the three friends were sitting in the Riverview cafeteria, which was filled with the lunchtime crowd. Their table commanded a spectacular view of the city's iron bridge through its smoked-glass windows.

Clare cut her off. "What's this? What are you talking about, Karen? Something I should know about?"

"I think so," said Karen. "I was walking my patient in the hallway when—what was his name?—Dr. Mackey started yelling at a nurse to give medicine. The nurse was Ellen Garrison, and she told him the patient was allergic to Valium. She had written that in the nurses' notes. All I can tell you is, it was clear to me that he never read Ellen's notes.''

Clare seemed a little embarrassed. "I'm aware of this kind of problem. The nurses' notes being separate makes them easy to forget.''

"It seems so backward," Karen said. "At St. Barnabas the notes are all together in chronological order.''

Joan piped up. "Well, the nurses' notes and the doctors' notes are together here too.''

"Come on, Joan, you know perfectly well we're not

talking about a highly specialized sixteen-bed unit like yours," said Clare. "We're talking about the whole hospital."

"That woman could have died," said Karen.

Joan laughed. "Oh, come on. Don't be so dramatic. Phil Mackey's no fool. Things like this happen. You know, they happen to nurses too."

Clare said, "That's just the point, Joan. It shouldn't happen to anyone. And it's less likely to if my proposal goes through."

"What proposal?" asked Karen.

"Next month, at the June meeting, the board will vote on a proposal I made to integrate the progress notes."

"Terrific, Clare," Karen said enthusiastically.

"Even with a cheerleader like Karen here," said Joan, "you can forget about your proposal getting past the board. Phil Mackey told me it's dead in the water."

"Phil Mackey doesn't know everything," Clare said defensively. "When I was working on the proposal, many people expressed their support."

"Who? The janitor?" asked Joan, laughing.

Karen said, "Well, I think it's a great idea, Clare. It works at St. Barnabas and it could work at Riverview. I'm a hundred percent for it."

"It looks like I've got one friend a hundred percent for it and one a hundred percent against it," said Clare, looking at Joan.

"That's not true," said Joan. She paused. "Actually," she drawled, "I'm a hundred and twelve percent against it."

# TWO

## June

Joan sat at the nurses' station, taking report over the phone from an operating-room nurse. As they spoke, her eyes idly scanned the dozen TV monitors which covered all the beds she could not see directly from where she sat. The Surgical Intensive Care Unit was quiet, except for the hum and whir of dozens of electronic devices, without which few of these patients would remain alive. The SICU was the juncture of the most advanced scientific technology and medical art. Right now, Joan Fisher sat at the center, controlling that world.

It was just after six in the evening. The day shift and most of the administrators had gone home. Things were settling down for the evening. Joan loved that feeling of the hospital after dusk. It felt somehow more like "her place" when the brass was gone and the workers were in charge.

Riverview's SICU was a sixteen-bed unit. Although this unit was mainly for surgical patients, occasionally some medical cases were admitted. The SICU was located in the new part of the hospital and was exemplary—well staffed, well endowed, and well maintained.

"Are you sure this is one of my cases?" Joan was asking. The operating-room nurse at the other end bristled. "The patient is a sixty-five-year-old woman with diabetes and a broken hip. What other qualifications does she need for entry into your unit, Miss Fisher? Look, this isn't my order. Do you want me to put the doctor on? Actually, you might like to talk to him."

It was a familiar game: I'll tell teacher on you! Joan said sharply, "That won't be necessary. Send her over. For the future, this unit is for seriously ill people, it's not a baby-sitting service." The words reverberated in her mind in a hollow-sounding way. This only happened when she was tired, and she was more tired than she thought. She needed a pick-me-up. Maybe even a vacation.

Her thoughts were interrupted by the voice on the phone. "Look, this isn't my fault." The woman spoke softly, so that no one else around her could hear. "Going by her age and condition, a case can be made that she belongs in the SICU. You'll only have her for a few days until her insulin requirements are stabilized."

"Okay, we'll be ready to receive her," said Joan wearily. She was mainly arguing as a matter of principle, really. If she didn't put up some resistance she would open the floodgates to the unit and every doctor and nurse in the hospital would be shipping their difficult cases there. As it was, the SICU was so busy that Riverview sometimes had to use ordinary recovery rooms as auxiliary intensive care units.

Joan poured herself a cup of black coffee. She had awakened at around noon with a smashing hangover and taken two aspirin. The headache was returning, centering around her eyes. She decided to make a quick tour of the unit, checking each patient against the Kardex file, a plastic index.

She saw the resident, Dr. Bijan, and discussed a few of the cases with him. He was a surgeon in training, hardworking and ambitious. All the surgical residents dreamed of being rich and powerful. In the meantime they took a fair amount of abuse from the senior surgeons. Bijan was beginning a one-year fellowship in the unit. She had only known him a month, and she liked him. He was fun to be around.

Suddenly the doors opened with a mechanical whoosh and a transporter, aided by a nurse, pushed the new patient, Mrs. Anna Bloom, into the SICU. She was only semiconscious. They positioned her with pillows. Joan washed her hands and returned to help them.

"How are you feeling?" she asked.

Mrs. Bloom just groaned weakly. She was still under the influence of the anesthesia from her hip operation.

Joan reached under the covers, found Mrs. Bloom's hand, and spoke some reassuring words. "You're in a special unit, Mrs. Bloom, where we will be able to watch you very carefully. Our first job is to get you off the stretcher and into your bed here."

Joan looked around. The transporter who had been helping with the gurney had disappeared. At first Joan couldn't see anyone who wasn't busy.

"Transfer!" she yelled out, rather harshly. This was a signal to all the nurses in her unit to assess their priorities and see if they could get away from their primary patients to help make a transfer. The transporter returned and two nurses responded. They stood on one side of the gurney while Joan and the transporter stood on the other. Mrs. Bloom's legs were propped with orthopedic pillows to hold the affected hip in the proper alignment. She was a short woman, fully packed, and the more conscious she became, the more frightened she was. Joan spoke to her crew with calm efficiency.

"Let's use the bottom sheet as a lifter and move her to the edge of the bed. At the count of three . . ." Joan counted and each member of the team lifted a different corner of the sheet under Mrs. Bloom's body. They moved her as a unit to the edge of the bed.

Suddenly Mrs. Bloom came alive. "Help!" she screamed at the top of her lungs. "Help me, somebody!" With her heavy accent, it sounded somewhat comical to Joan.

Joan tried to calm her down. "We *are* helping you, Mrs. Bloom. You are almost there, dear."

"God, this woman is heavier than she looks," said the transporter. One of the nurses gave him a silencing look.

"You're almost on the bed," Joan repeated. "Now just try to relax and don't . . ."

"Please, you're murdering me!" screamed Mrs. Bloom, struggling.

". . . don't fight us, please, Mrs. Bloom," Joan said through clenched teeth. She nodded her head as a signal and once again, with a huge effort, the team practically hurled the patient onto the bed. At that moment Joan felt a blinding flash of pain in her lower back. Luckily she was able to catch onto the cold steel of the gurney rail and push down on it, to give herself some relief. Movement to the right or left was painful.

"What is it, Joan, your back again?" asked one of the younger nurses.

"I'll be all right."

"What about me!" Mrs. Bloom bellowed. "*I'm* the patient."

Joan motioned to Sarah, the nurse whom she trusted the most, a tall and attractive black woman in her early twenties. Her close-cropped hair accentuated a beautiful, long neck. "Take over for me. Get the vital signs and finish admitting her."

Joan went into the nurses' break room to rest. She felt better after sitting for a few minutes, but she wondered what would happen when she stood up.

A few minutes later Sarah came in and said, "Mr. Bloom is looking for his wife."

"I don't need a conversation with Mr. Bloom. I need a stiff drink." Sarah smiled and went to hold off the anxious husband. Joan stood up slowly and, with a feeling of gratitude, noted her back was somewhat better. She could stand in one place with relative ease. She could hear Mr. Bloom outside the door, arguing with Sarah. Joan went into the hall. "I'll take over now," she said.

Morris Bloom was pacing up and down the cramped hallway, which was lined on one side with empty beds. He was a small man, nattily dressed, with the kind of bank clerk's gray mustache Joan thought had gone out with the forties.

"This is one heck of a place you have here, let me tell you," said Mr. Bloom. He had the same accent as his wife. "One heck of a place." He wasn't shy, thought Joan.

"My name is Joan Fisher," she said. "I'm the head nurse in charge of the Surgical Intensive Care Unit."

This seemed to quiet him down. "I don't know how a person is supposed to find his way around here," he said. He glanced at her head. "I stopped three women I thought were nurses and they turned out to be cleaning women."

"Housekeepers," Joan said.

"You can't tell one person from another. Why don't you at least wear a cap so that everyone will know who you are?" he asked.

"I really don't know the historical reason behind the

change in nursing attire," she said, trying to hide her sarcasm. "Now, Mr. Bloom, I would like to take you in to see your wife."

"That's what I'm here for," he said nervously.

Mrs. Bloom was still moaning to herself. "Mrs. Bloom, can you tell me where you are?" Joan asked.

"The hospital," she said slowly.

"Very good," said Joan. "You're in a special part of the hospital. You will probably only be here for a few days. Here's your husband. I let him come in for a few minutes."

"Morris," she said, groaning. He leaned over and kissed her.

Suddenly, seeing him standing there, blinking, his fedora in hand, Joan felt sorry for him. Mr. Bloom was simply overwhelmed by his wife's fall that morning, the strange procedures, the sterile environment. He was just a frightened old man, blinking up at his wife's monitors.

"Mr. Bloom," Joan said finally, "now that you have said hello I would like you to wait outside while we take some tests. When we finish I'll come and bring you in."

"Please, Miss Fischler, let me stay—" Morris began. He was interrupted by a gut-wrenching scream emanating from a nearby bed. A neuro patient was being turned onto his side. Bloom jumped visibly, and Mrs. Bloom began to groan again. After that horrendous scream Mr. Bloom was ready to leave. Joan felt he was putting up a fuss more to make his wife feel good than out of any overwhelming desire to stay. After he left, Joan drew three tubes of blood to be tested.

She was just finishing when Sarah asked, "Have you done your daily administrative report?"

"No, I haven't had time yet," she said, exhaling in frustration. The unit, with Mrs. Bloom, was now completely full. It would take her a good half hour to fill in the report. Joan gave special attention to the multiple trauma injuries and the cancer sugical cases who occupied most of the beds.

Every day that week Joan called around the hospital to try to get Mrs. Bloom transferred out of her unit. There was simply no bed available on the ortho floor, where she really belonged. By the end of the week Joan had completely lost her patience. Mrs. Bloom's insulin requirements were stable and she was annoying Joan with her constant moaning, complaining, and nosiness about the other patients in the unit.

Her efforts to teach Mrs. Bloom some exercises had all ended in frustration. She decided to try one more time. "Mrs. Bloom, I'm going to show you how to do some breathing exercises now."

"At my age I have to learn how to breathe?" she asked with her heavy inflection.

"It's very important, when you've had surgery, that you breathe correctly. Otherwise you could develop pneumonia."

"You know, I always hear about people getting pneumonia in the hospital, but I never knew why. Is that what happened to him?" She gestured to the neuro case on the right.

Joan sighed and tried to ignore her. "The basic idea is this: I want you to take two very deep breaths. Hold them as long as you can"—she demonstrated—"and then let them out. After that, I want you to cough."

"It seems silly, Nurse. I don't have to cough," Mrs. Bloom objected. "Probably if I started coughing you'd want to give me cough syrup. I don't want that. Frankly, I hate the taste of it."

"This is part of your treatment," said Joan, sighing.

"Part of getting better. You have to force it. Take one deep breath," she said a little impatiently.

Mrs. Bloom got halfway through a breath and gasped, "It hurts!"

"Try again, Mrs. Bloom," said Joan.

She tried again, got through two rather shallow breaths, and then coughed—more like an "ahem" than a real cough. "Just awful, Nurse," she said. "I feel like I'm tearing up my hip operation. It hurts so much! Like all the stitches are coming out. He sews me up and then you have me tear the whole thing apart."

"I know it feels like you're hurting yourself, but it's important to stretch your lungs. You're just straining a few little capillaries, blood vessels."

"Terrible, terrible," said Mrs. Bloom, exhausted.

"Please try again," said Joan.

"I can't . . ." said Mrs. Bloom, whimpering.

"Okay," said Joan. "I'm going to give you this little device we call an 'incentive spirometer.' You just suck on this strawlike thing and you'll see the meter go up to 200. Your 'incentive' is to get it up to 400, then 600. It measures the amount of air getting into your lungs."

"Some incentive! I'll try later." She paused. "Nurse, I have to apologize to you. Is your back feeling better today? I'm sorry about last week, but all I could think about was that I was afraid."

"That's perfectly normal, Mrs. Bloom," said Joan. "I would have done the same thing. Anyway, it's feeling much better every day."

"Oh, that's wonderful. And when you go out, if you see my husband, would you tell him I'm feeling a little bit better, too? Why should he have to worry?"

Joan found Morris Bloom waiting patiently on a chair in the corridor. He jumped up and met her halfway as she approached. "Miss Fischler, I've been thinking. I'm awfully worried about her. Why can't she get out of this special unit already?"

"I just came from your wife, Mr. Bloom. She's doing remarkably well. In fact, she just sent me out to tell you how much better she's feeling. She's working on her breathing exercises and can't be disturbed now." She embellished a little. "She said that you have to take care of yourself, Mr. Bloom, and that she needs you to be strong. You know, she's going to have a long period of recuperation. A hip like this doesn't heal in a day." She was beginning, unconsciously, to lapse into Morris' speech patterns.

"But she's doing well?" he asked, seizing on the hope held out to him.

Joan looked through the file, which she had in her hand. It contained the latest results from Mrs. Bloom's tests. The blood tests were remarkably good. She wondered again why the day shift hadn't arranged her transfer.

"Superbly. Mr. Bloom, you need to take it easy," said Joan. "She's not going to be in the unit long, I can assure you of that."

"I see . . . I see," said Mr. Bloom. He wasn't following everything she was saying. What he did follow was her soothing tone: his wife was not going to die—in fact she was getting better. Having lived with her "sugar diabetes" for over twenty years, he was always expecting disaster to cut them down at the next turn. Blindness, insulin shock, amputations. So far, nothing terrible had happened.

Joan had turned back to the unit when around the corner came Bob Miller, her ex-husband. They hadn't seen each other in over a month. Bob was always busy these days, going to meetings and conferences. Besides, he made rounds early in the day, while Joan only worked the afternoon shift.

"Why, hello, Mr. Bloom," he said effusively. "I'm Dr. Miller, one of the doctors who operated on your wife." So smooth, Joan thought. The two men shook hands.

"They told me you were away on a special case," said Morris Bloom. He seemed impressed. "Doctor, please tell me the truth, how is my wife?"

"That's what I'm here for, to find out," said Bob. "After I do I will give you a full report. Sorry I haven't talked to you before, but I've been away at a medical conference. Oh, hello, Joan," he said as if he hadn't seen her before.

"Hello, Doctor," she said coolly. "Can I talk to you for a second? Excuse us for a moment, Mr. Bloom." She drew him aside, out of earshot. Mr. Bloom fished through his wallet for a list of questions he had written down. "So, you look good," she said, looking him up and down. He was tall and skinny, with curly hair already graying at the temples. "Is that a gun in your pocket or are you just glad to see me?"

Bob knew Joan too well to be thrown off guard by this. "Same old Joan," he said, more than a little annoyed.

"You know, Bob, every time I make a payment on our condo loan"—she emphasized the word "our"—"I regret that I refused to take any alimony from you."

"What about your feminist principles? I really respected you for that."

She cringed. "I bet you did."

"Excuse me, Doctor, but she's in terrible pain," said Mr. Bloom, breaking into their tête-à-tête.

"Excuse me, Mr. Bloom, but that's not true," Joan said. "Her pain is completely under control."

"Ms. Fisher, I'd like Mrs. Bloom to have something for her pain," Bob said in his most authoritative voice.

"She just had her meds," said Joan, unable to hide her irritation. "She's not due for another couple of hours."

"That's okay," Bob said, accepting the challenge. "What you gave her before was probably too weak. I'll write an order for more medication after I see her."

"And I'll wait to give her additional meds until you've seen her." Joan turned on her heel. She went into the unit and made rounds quickly. Everything was under control, but she couldn't shake her feeling of irritation.

Sarah asked, "Are you going to get that Mrs. Bloom out of here tonight?"

"I'll try, but Bob's the doctor. He's giving me a hard time, as usual. Well, I've got a lot of cases to worry about." Sarah nodded sympathetically. They were interrupted by sounds of distress coming from the corridor. "Oh, Jesus H. Christ!" Joan said, in annoyance, and rushed out. She found Mr. Bloom sobbing.

"What the hell did you say to him?" she hissed at Bob.

"Don't talk to me that way!" he commanded.

"What's the matter, Mr. Bloom?" she said, soothingly putting her arm around him.

He shook her off. "You lied to me, that's what the matter is," he said, turning all his anger on her.

"*I* lied to you?" she asked in amazement.

"Yes, you told me everything was okay, that she was fine and would be out with the regular patients soon."

"Mr. Bloom, I—"

"Now the doctor comes and tells me *the truth*. That she may never walk again! That the bone in her hip may *rot*—"

"Wait a minute!" Bob began. "It's true that necrosis under certain circumstances might—" But no one was listening.

"That she might even *die*. . . ."

Joan sighed. "Mr. Bloom, your wife has had a terrible

accident. She is comfortable and stable in intensive care and has been for a week. We *all* expect her to recover. Don't we, Dr. Miller?"

Mr. Bloom looked searchingly at the doctor.

"Ms. Fisher is correct. We *do* expect her to recover. I'd better go in and check her now."

"Sure, you do that," said Joan. Mr. Bloom pressed his lips tightly together and walked toward the men's room in an attempt to compose himself. Joan followed Bob into the unit. He could feel the anger coming off her in waves.

"Look, I merely informed him of the various complications that were possible for a woman in her condition," Bob explained. "Don't look at me as though I said she was going to die," he added. "In no way did I tell him that she was going to develop any of those complications. That was just his misunderstanding. And if you hadn't come charging out there I would have had the whole thing straightened out in two seconds."

Joan glared at her ex-husband. "Bob, you could solve the problem by transferring her out tonight."

"Don't tell me what to do, Joan," he said irritably, and went off to examine Mrs. Bloom. Joan remained extremely agitated. The one thing she hated most was to be talked down to, especially by her ex-husband. She went out and got Mr. Bloom and spoke to him as they entered the unit together.

"Mr. Bloom, I haven't tried to keep you or your wife in the dark about her condition or anything else," she said. "In this unit patients are told everything. And it so happens that her condition is excellent."

"And yet the doctor said . . ."

Bob walked over to where they were talking. "Mr. Bloom, please try to cooperate with the nursing staff," he said in a conciliatory way. "Your wife is doing very well."

"Dr. Miller," Joan said bitterly, "can I have a word with you before you leave?"

"Certainly," said Bob, smiling uncertainly.

"Now, Mr. Bloom," said Joan, measuring out each word, "if you'll excuse me I'm going to talk to Dr. Miller privately for a moment. You can go and sit by your wife's bedside. That should reassure you that everything's okay." Mr. Bloom said nothing but made his way cautiously to her bed.

Bob followed Joan to the desk. The unit itself seemed calm. "Look, Joan, I don't have time for—"

"Bob, I have something to say to you, but I'd rather that the whole world not hear it. So I would appreciate it if you would just step into the utility room for a minute." The utility room was a small room off the main unit used for storing patient care supplies. Joan sometimes used it when she wanted to hold a private conversation.

Once in private, her words rushed out: "Don't you think you owe me an explanation?"

"I owe you?" he said, trying to claim the role of the calm one. This whole scene was familiar to both of them from their ill-fated marriage.

"Why did you find it necessary," she demanded, "to come barging onto my unit and destroy the very carefully constructed rapport I had established with that old man? You heard him: he accused me of *lying* to him about his wife's condition. What a crock!"

"So what? Nothing will ever come of it," Bob said, attempting nonchalance. "He's just confused, and that's all there is to it."

"But what gives you the *right*—"

"You just listen for a minute, Joan," Bob said, beginning to lose his temper. "Where do *you* come off dictating to me?

Let's face it: you don't have the right to tell me, or any other doctor, when to transfer patients."

"Oh, come on! We both know that's not the point," she said angrily. "You should have examined Mrs. Bloom and talked with the ICU staff before giving Mr. Bloom a speech about unlikely complications. And I see you're not above pulling rank to win an argument, are you?"

He was obviously unaffected by her attack. "It's just that a patient's family *must* be kept informed of every possibility. And while we're airing grievances, Joan," he continued, "was it necessary for you to criticize me in front of Mr. Bloom? If you want to know the truth, if you had stuck with medical school, you'd understand a lot better what a difficult position doctors are put in."

"That's ridiculous and simplistic."

"Joan, you and I both know you wouldn't dare to talk to any other doctor this way. It's only because we know each other so well—"

"No, it isn't," she interrupted. "As a matter of fact—" Just then Joan winced.

"What's the matter?" Bob asked, surprised.

"Oh, damn it, it's my back again," she whispered. He had seen enough of these attacks to understand the pain she was in.

"What brought this on?" He sounded concerned.

"I helped lift Mrs. Bloom onto her bed last week. She weighs a ton."

"I can't tell you what to do, but why don't you let the other nurses do the lifting?" Bob took her shoulders. "Look, let's forget about all this stupid business. The last thing you need right now is to be fighting with me." She was surprised at his sudden touch and stumbled into him. He reached out and gave her an affectionate hug. Once in touch, she wouldn't let go, and for a moment he breathed in the familiar and arousing odor of her hair. She turned her face toward his. As if by instinct, she kissed him on the mouth. It was all so familiar. She did not want the moment to end.

Bob pulled away abruptly, his face red. "Well, I hope that didn't make your back any worse," he said with a nervous laugh.

" 'S better," she mumbled. "All better. Bob," she added slowly. "You know, honey, if you want to . . ."

"I'm sorry, Joan," he said, trying to be gentle about it. "It's over. We've gone this route before. It never works." As he reached for the door to the unit he turned back and said, "Take care of yourself, Joan. I'll talk to the ortho floor and try to arrange Bloom's transfer for tomorrow. Thanks for keeping our misunderstanding private. I appreciate that."

Joan placed her cool palms on her flushed cheeks and closed her eyes for a moment. Life goes on; she had to make rounds.

Joan arrived at work at four o'clock the next afternoon. During report the phone rang and Sarah answered.

"That's great, Dr. Miller," said Sarah, and Joan looked up and took the phone from her.

"Joan," said Bob Miller curtly, "I'm on the ortho floor and they finally have a bed. Do me a favor and tell the Blooms she's moving tomorrow." He paused, as if waiting for her to thank him, but she wasn't about to give him the satisfaction.

"No problem," she said. "See you." And she hung up.

"Well, I have good news for you," Joan said, approaching the elderly couple. "Dr. Miller has arranged your transfer tomorrow."

"What?" said Bloom angrily. "She's not ready for this."

"What about my special bed?" asked Mrs. Bloom, sounding scared.

Joan cut them off, impatiently. "You are ready, Mrs. Bloom, and your trapeze and bed will go with you."

"But I'm used to things here. Morris," she said plaintively.

"Medically you've been ready to leave for a week."

"Does she have to?" asked Mr. Bloom. "She gets such special care here, especially from you and Sarah." His voice was cajoling.

Joan smiled. There was no way they were going to stay on her unit past tomorrow. "Absolutely," said Joan.

"Well, maybe we could get a private nurse to take care of her," said Mr. Bloom.

"That's not a bad idea," said Joan cautiously. "But, you know, it could be expensive."

Mr. Bloom seemed slightly offended. "If that's what it takes," he said proudly, "that's what we have the savings account for. They always say you should save for a rainy day. I guess this is that day."

Mrs. Bloom looked interested. "Can we find one as nice as you?" she asked.

"Much nicer," said Joan, laughing. "In fact, I can recommend one to you. Her name is Karen Bovit."

"Bovit?" said Morris Bloom. "What kind of name is that?"

"It's Lithuanian," said Karen, sighing inwardly. It was the third time that week they had gone through this routine.

It had been a busy week. Eric had gone home on Sunday. He still had his colostomy but was planning to graduate anyway. Karen had been glad when she got Joan's call. Now she was beginning to wonder.

"Are you sure you're not Jewish?" asked Mr. Bloom. "You're so intelligent, and beautiful, too."

Karen smiled.

"I'm from Russia," said Mr. Bloom. "That's not far from Lithuania. My wife's from Hungary. Which reminds me, did I ever tell you how to make a Hungarian omelet?" asked Mr. Bloom. "First you steal two eggs . . ."

Karen tried to laugh. It was hard. But Mrs. Bloom laughed delightedly. "I bet it's not often you have such an easy job."

Karen glanced at her watch. "I'm going to take my lunch break now," she said.

"Go ahead, Miss Bovit," said Mr. Bloom softly. "I'll take care of her. I've done so for almost forty years."

Karen was glad to get outside. The sunlight was dazzling, although it was a cool day for June. Everyone complained that summer had not begun yet, but Karen liked the feel of the cool breeze in her hair. She ran into Clare on the street, hurrying back from the deli with a yogurt and an apple.

"Karen, I didn't even know you were working this week! You should have called me," she said.

"I'm on the Bloom case," said Karen, sighing. "Remind me to stop by the SICU to thank Joan for the referral. What a pal."

"Have you had lunch?" Clare asked.

"This is my lunch hour, but I was planning to go for a walk. You know me, Clare, I'm on a perpetual diet."

"Well then, you might as well come back to my office," said Clare warmly. "We can catch up."

"Charlotte Morgan called," said Betty when they walked in. "How are you?" she added, to Karen.

"Fine," said Karen.

"She said it was urgent," Betty added, a bit self-importantly.

"I'll call her as soon as I finish lunch," said Clare calmly. Betty shrugged and turned back to her computer.

"You know, I don't think Joan handed me the Bloom case out of friendship," said Karen. "She wants to test my ability to be patient."

Clare laughed easily. "I've met the Blooms on rounds. Did you hear the one about the Hungarian omelet?"

Karen giggled. "Four times this week. Remind me to tell it to Joan. Over and over and over again."

They had a good laugh at this. "Joan doesn't always have the greatest tolerance for the foibles of mankind, does she?" Clare said.

"That's putting it mildly. You know," Karen said thoughtfully, "Joan doesn't seem very happy to me."

"Well, the years do take their toll," said Clare, sighing. "She's had a hard time of it. We all change, I guess."

"What disturbs me is how little she has changed. I mean, what worked at twenty seems so tired and sad at thirty."

"Philip Mackey," said Clare, nodding. "Look, I've really got to call Charlotte Morgan." Karen stood up to leave. "I didn't mean to kick you out. Let's get together again soon, okay?"

At that very moment on the other side of the world the *Bluebonnet*, a power-assisted sailing ship out of Newport Beach, California, was entering the tiny harbor of Nerja, Spain.

Heather Asher stood on the deck, admiring the tall cliffs. "That must be the Balcón de Europa. It's in all the guidebooks. Norton," she yelled, over the sound of the engine, "better steer clear of those rocks. They look really treacherous." The wind whipped her attractive gray hair back from her temples.

"Don't worry," he said, laughing. "They're clearly marked on the charts." The navigational charts were Norton's Bible.

"Isn't this beautiful!" she exclaimed. "See those people up there? That looks like a restaurant cut into the cliff."

A rowboat came out to greet them. In excellent Spanish, Heather greeted the grizzled, one-eyed rower who introduced himself as the harbor master. She arranged for a two-night mooring. Then the two of them trekked up the beach and into the white-walled town.

"Are you all right?" Norton asked when they reached the top.

"Just a little out of breath, that's all," said Heather, panting. "You've always made me breathless, and you know it!"

The two walked hand in hand, except when a car or motorbike forced its way down the tiny alleys. They looked in at the shoe stores and the open-air stalls selling the usual tourist curios.

"Here's our chance to stock up on wine, Norton," Heather said enthusiastically. "Can you believe the price of this sherry? This stuff is only a dollar a bottle!"

He laughed. "This is really lovely," he said. "It's hard to believe places like this really exist."

They found a restaurant on a side street which had piped-in flamenco music. Norton had some gazpacho and salad, while Heather ordered the paella. "Do you think it's safe?" she asked, looking at the yellow rice. The fish seemed fresh, the chicken was succulent. Saffron had been laid on with a generous hand.

They relaxed after dinner with a couple of cold beers. After sauntering back to the harbor they went to sleep on the gently rocking boat. It was a warm June for Spain. Africa was just across the water. They thought perhaps they might visit there next.

In the middle of the night Heather spoke gently to

Norton. She knew his breathing patterns well enough to know that he was asleep.

"I feel awful," she moaned.

"Your stomach?" he asked.

She was silent. "I don't now. Something." Her voice was weak.

Heather was not a complainer, and Norton immediately sensed this was serious. He turned on the light, leaned over, and looked at her. "Oh, my God," was his first reaction.

"What is it, Norton?" she asked, frightened.

"Look at you," he said. "You've turned yellow."

Heather grabbed the mirror. Her skin, and especially her eyes, were indeed yellow.

"What could it be?" he wondered aloud, his face looking increasingly anxious. "Hepatitis? I bet the shellfish was bad."

"Well, maybe they just put too much saffron in the paella," Heather joked. She felt hollow inside and rested her perspiring head back on the hard bunk pillow. "It's probably nothing. Let's just wait till morning and see if it goes away by itself."

# THREE

*July*

Betty stood in the doorway of Clare's office, a pink sheet of paper in her hand. "You won't believe what I just found in the loo," she said, laughing.

Clare looked up from her desk. She had gotten in early and was already hard at work on the department's monthly staff census.

"The loo?" asked Clare, smiling. Her secretary had spent last summer in England and come back with a ready supply of Britishisms.

"The toy-let," she said, suddenly switching to a comic "chewing gum" accent.

"Okay, tell me. What did you find in the toilet? And this better not be a bad joke."

"Well, that depends on your point of view," said Betty, relishing her secret and enjoying her boss's impatience. "Okay, here it is," she said, handing it over. "I found it taped to the mirror at eye level."

Clare immediately recognized the pink sheet as part of the Riverview Hospital chart, paper imprinted with the words NURSES' NOTES. It had two holes on the top for insertion into the patient charts.

"I also noticed a stack of them out on the landing!" Betty said excitedly. "Someone's obviously run them through a copying machine. Pretty clever, if you ask me!" Clare read to herself:

## ARE YOU A PROFESSIONAL?

Fellow Nurses—Are you a professional? Haven't you received specialized training in one of the most arduous of all professions? Of course! Then why are your notes ignored?

Not long ago a patient almost DIED when a doctor failed to read the nurse's notes!

This is not an isolated incident. It will happen again.

A proposal has been made to integrate nurses' and doctors' notes. We must support it! "Monster Morgan" wants to keep nurses in their place.

WE ARE PROFESSIONALS. WE MUST PROTECT OUR PATIENTS!

—RANK-AND-FILE NURSES

Clare said nothing. "You say these are around the hospital?" she asked finally. Her voice was unnaturally subdued.

"From what I can gather. Of course, I can get on the grapevine and find out for you, if you like. Or I can dust them for prints."

"Betty, be serious. You realize how damaging this could be, don't you?" Betty nodded. "My proposal was supposed to be confidential." She glanced down at the leaflet.

"Well, you obviously have admirers—"

"Sure," said Clare with a touch of bitterness. "More like enemies."

"How so?" said Betty.

"This is just awful! 'Monster Morgan!' This makes my proposal look childish."

"What a spot!" said Betty, relishing the excitement. "If you back out now you're going to lose face."

"And if I keep going with the proposal I'm going to be tarred with the same brush. It's really quite brilliant." She threw down the pink paper in disgust.

Betty pondered the situation for a moment. "I admit that sometimes I can't help listening to other people's conversations. I overheard Dr. Mackey telling your friend Joan he thought it was a stupid idea. Maybe Dr. Mackey . . ."

Clare was not about to be drawn into a conversation about professional colleagues. "Well, let's drop it for now," she said. "I need some time to think this over. If you hear anything else, please let me know."

"Okay," Betty said enthusiastically.

Clare watched her secretary go out. She had a quirky "punk" style. For instance, she wore outlandish rings on every finger—except the one that mattered, Clare thought to herself. Yet, in a way, Clare had grown to like her.

Soon afterward Charlotte Morgan called Clare in for a conference. The nursing director's office was down the hall, on the twentieth floor of the new hospital building. Above her secretary's desk was an ornately framed engraving of an early nurse holding a dying soldier.

Charlotte's secretary was not there, so Clare simply knocked on the nursing director's door. She heard a voice say, "Come in."

"Clare, I'm glad you're here," said Charlotte amiably, as she entered. Charlotte Morgan was a woman in her early sixties, a bit clownish-looking, with rubbery features on a smallish face. Her hair was permed in a neat bouffant. She tended to overdress.

"How's your husband feeling?" Clare asked considerately.

"Just fine." Charlotte seemed uncomfortable discussing personal matters. "I'll tell him you asked for him. . . . Now, first of all, Clare," she said, abruptly changing the topic, "I'd like to see an article in *Riverview Progress* on the drop in last month's infection statistics. Do you think you could talk to our PR director about that?"

"No problem," said Clare, waiting politely.

"Next, about the rank-and-file leaflets," Charlotte said, trying unsuccessfully to appear nonchalant. "Do we have any idea who's behind this yet?"

"Not exactly," said Clare. "I did see Ellen Garrison handing them out in the Astor Pavilion lobby."

"Who's Ellen Garrison?" Charlotte asked.

Clare felt uncomfortable. "She's a very bright young nurse, working on Astor Ten. She's even applied for a transfer to the SICU."

"The only transfer she's going to get is right out of here," Charlotte said vehemently. "If I'm not mistaken, Dr. Mackey approached me last week and complained about her attitude."

"There's two sides to every story," Clare added hastily. "I've heard a different version of that incident."

"Nevertheless, Clare," Charlotte said, "I want you to fire her."

Clare was momentarily thrown off balance. "On what grounds?"

"Stealing hospital property, for starters," Charlotte said. "You saw her handing out leaflets. And I did too. In case you didn't notice, they're printed on hospital stationery."

Clare felt her back was against the wall. "Ellen's very young, Charlotte, and she's a good nurse. Why don't we just suspend her?" she suggested, looking for a way out.

"Clare, you're reaching," Charlotte said with a little laugh. "Riverview Hospital policy is very clear. You steal, you get fired. I want you to take care of it this week."

Clare wanted to complain, but Charlotte's firm tone of voice left no room for any further discussion.

Clare didn't feel like going back to her office. She decided to put off firing Ellen for a few days. Instead, she dropped in on a few floors where there had been problems recently. On Astor Seven she was confronted by an agitated nurse's aide, Amy Green. "Oh, Ms. Henson, am I glad to see you!" she said.

"Well, it's nice to feel needed," said Clare in an attempt at lightness. "What's the problem, Amy?"

Amy was not going to be humored. "It's that new graduate nurse, Joyce Rogers. You've got to get her to stop instituting new procedures with no explanation."

"For instance?" asked Clare. Ordinarily she would have been impatient with this sort of thing, but today it provided a welcome distraction.

"For instance, she has us all down on our hands and knees scrubbing IV poles. Now, I ask you, is that right? That's not in our job description, is it? Scrubbing poles! I'm a nurse's aide, Ms. Henson, not a housekeeper." She spoke that word with condescension. "If you would like my opinion, Ms. Henson," she said in a lowered voice, "you should get rid of this Joyce Rogers."

"Just a minute now," said Clare angrily. She took a deep breath: her resentment over the run-in with Charlotte was in danger of bursting out inappropriately. "Okay, Amy, let's go talk to Joyce Rogers about this. Quite frankly, I don't want or need your suggestions on whom to get rid of or whom to keep."

"Sure, Ms. Henson," said the aide. "But please do something about this before there's trouble."

They looked all over the floor but Joyce was nowhere to be found. Finally Clare opened the utility room and found Joyce Rogers kneeling on the floor. On her knees she had knee pads fashioned from gauze bandages.

"Uh, Miss Rogers," said Clare, smiling, "would you mind giving me a moment of your time?"

She was a small woman of about thirty, a Southerner with long blond hair and very blue eyes. Her nose was upturned, almost pug. When she saw Clare her fair skin turned crimson.

"Now I know you're wondering what I'm doing down here on my hands and knees," she said, jumping up deftly. She pulled nervously at her rubber gloves, which wouldn't come off, adding to her embarrassment. "Do you know that these poles have not been cleaned in *months?* You should have seen the accumulated filth, the vile organic wastes—"

"Okay, Miss Rogers," said Clare. "I get the point. There's no need to make me lose my breakfast."

Joyce Rogers' large and supple mouth tightened in anger. "Well! I'm only trying to do my job and fulfill my oath as a nurse," said Joyce huffily. "I would think you would be supportive."

"I'm sorry," said Clare, realizing her mistake. "It's been a bad morning. I *do* appreciate your energy and zeal. But," she asked very gently, "don't we have a housekeeping staff to do this sort of thing? I mean, is it really necessary for you to spend your valuable time, including the time of your staff, scrubbing poles?"

"Housekeeping! They won't do it," Joyce Rogers said, happy at last to be able to vent her anger. "They refuse!

They tell me that it is 'patient equipment.' Well, I showed them. I just made these knee pads and set to work. They're a bunch of lazy, shiftless good-for-nothings." It didn't escape Clare's notice that Joyce Rogers was from the South—the inflections in her voice made that clear—and the housekeeping staff was mainly black. "They just plain refused. Those people just don't want to work. In housekeeping," she added.

"Miss Rogers, the housekeepers at this hospital have a job description that clearly states that patient equipment is nursing's responsibility."

Joyce was silent. "You know that I'm new here," she said finally.

"What were the names," Clare asked, "of the housekeeping staff who refused to work?"

"I don't know their names. . . ."

"We all look the same," Amy stage-whispered to Clare. She herself was half black, half Puerto Rican.

"That's quite enough, Amy," said Clare. "You can go now. Thank you very much," she added more softly. "If I need you, Amy, I'll call you."

"You see, the housekeepers refuse to even help wash the IV poles. I told that woman Amy what I told the rest of the nursing staff. We must be responsible for providing a safe environment for our patients. People talk about cleanliness being next to godliness. Did you ever stop to think about the amount of disease spread by microorganisms on things like IV poles alone? I mean, for mercy's sake, where do they think diseases come from?"

Clare looked around. A knot of nurse's aides had gathered a safe distance away, giggling. She saw it all clearly: Joyce had appeared perfectly normal when Clare hired her; but she was obviously a cleaning nut. Nevertheless, despite her heavy emotional involvement, she did have a point. And Clare also knew that this kind of fanaticism could be useful in a hospital setting.

"Miss Rogers, what you have done here is identify a very real problem," said Clare diplomatically. "However, I think there should be a meeting of the staff to decide how to solve the problem you have put your finger on."

"With all due respect, Ms. Henson," said Joyce, her eyelashes flapping nervously, "I think I know how to solve it. If everyone would pitch in, put on their gloves, and—"

"No, Miss Rogers, I think there has to be a better way. After all, you've already had to disrupt the morning baths in order to wash the poles. And I think that the patients' baths are more important, don't you?"

Joyce Rogers thought this over. "The poles are very important. If you could have seen them—they were disgusting." Her normally fair cheeks were crimson.

"I appreciate that," said Clare, using her most persuasive tone. "I really do. And believe me, I am not criticizing you. Your enthusiasm and judgment are remarkable and we need a lot more of that." She said this loud enough so the gaggle of aides could hear her. "I just think it is the Riverview way not to rush ahead and adopt new policies but to discuss the problem, explain it to the staff, and together come up with the best plan. Things work so much better that way, don't you agree?"

A patient bell rang down the corridor. A moment later a staff nurse, who had missed the whole scene, came to the door. "Oh, hello, Ms. Henson. Joyce, do you think I could have some help with a dressing change?" Reluctantly, Joyce nodded and began removing her knee pads—beaten in this battle but not the war.

The next day Clare checked over her list of things to do. She looked forward to her lunch date with Joan and Karen.

She needed to unburden herself. Firing Ellen Garrison loomed before her, uppermost on her list.

At the coffee shop, Clare caught sight of Karen sitting alone in a booth. She waved, made her way over, and sat down.

"So, what did the Hensons do on the Fourth of July?" asked Karen.

Clare smiled. Karen's sincere interest in her family gave her pleasure. "We took the kids to the fireworks. They had a ball. How about you?"

"As a matter of fact, I worked." Sensing Clare's surprise, she added, "Mrs. Bloom was feeling a little low."

"Mrs. Bloom? Is she still in the hospital?" asked Clare.

"You know hip injuries," said Karen.

"So where do you think Joan is?" Clare asked, looking at her watch.

"I think that's her coming down the street," said Karen, looking out the plate glass window.

Joan came in, looking as if she had just rolled out of bed. "Hi, guys. Order yet?" she asked, sliding into the booth next to Clare. The waitress came over and Clare asked for the cottage cheese plate. Karen decided on the Greek salad.

"I'll have the chili con carne," said Joan. "And"—she thought for a moment—"bring a draft beer with that. And lots of saltines. So, tell me, Karen," she asked with a touch of malice, "how are the Blabbering Blooms?"

"Happy to be rid of them, aren't you? Actually," said Karen, "they're lovely people."

Joan turned toward Clare. "It's hard to have lunch with a saint, isn't it?"

The waitress returned with their orders.

Picking at her cottage cheese plate, Clare said, "I'm a little upset about something. Would you give me your word that what I say won't leave this table?"

Her friends looked quizzically at each other. "Sure," said Karen for both of them.

"You know Ellen Garrison, the nurse on Astor Ten?" Her friends nodded. "I saw her handing out the rank-and-file leaflets. That would have been tolerable, but Charlotte Morgan saw her too."

"You mean Monster Morgan?" Joan asked, laughing.

"That's not funny, Joan. It so happens I'm firing Ellen this afternoon."

"For what?" asked Karen, astounded. "Expressing her opinion?"

"Technically, for stealing hospital property. Really, because I was directed to by Charlotte."

"You're not going to do it, are you?" Karen asked. She sounded disgusted. "She's a great nurse. If it hadn't been for her that patient could have died."

"I feel terrible about it," said Clare. "That's why I'm mentioning it to you."

"I don't," said Joan. "She has a bad attitude." She drained the rest of her beer. "These glasses get smaller and smaller."

"How do you know she wasn't just handing them out for a friend?" said Karen.

"That's not the issue," said Clare. "I just wanted to tell you because I feel so bad about it and I didn't want you to hear a distorted version."

"It goes with the territory," said Joan.

"That's why I'd never want to be in management," said Karen. "I don't envy you."

It wasn't until the end of the week that Clare got around to calling Ellen into her office.

"Is anything wrong, Ms. Henson?" Ellen asked nervously. She was a young woman with olive complexion and keen, intelligent eyes.

"This is very hard for me," Clare began. "I saw you handing out those rank-and-file leaflets last week."

"Yes?" said Ellen.

"I'm sorry to inform you that you're being let go."

It took a moment for the meaning to sink in. "You mean you're firing me?"

"Yes, Ellen, I'm sorry."

Ellen's face turned red, blinking back tears. "You've got to be kidding, Ms. Henson. I just don't understand. Just for handing out leaflets on my own time . . ."

"The fact is," said Clare carefully, "you were observed in possession of stolen property. And that's the reason you're being let go."

"I didn't steal anything," Ellen said heatedly. "Some of the nurses have gotten together informally to try and figure out a way to protect the patients. Some of these doctors get away with murder! Just the other day I saved a patient's life on my unit. I have no idea where the stationery came from."

"Nonetheless, you were involved, and so far you're the only one who's been caught. You certainly couldn't expect us to take this lightly, could you, Ellen?"

Ellen began to cry softly. "I don't want to bring up personal matters, but I'm raising a child on my own. I can't get fired right now."

"I've arranged for you to get two weeks' severance pay, Ellen. That's the best I could do."

"What if I went to Charlotte Morgan herself?" she asked through her tears. "I'd like to have a chance to appeal this to her."

"Charlotte Morgan is the one who fired you," said Clare.

"Oh, God, what's the use?" said Ellen bitterly. "I can't

believe a nurse can be fired for supporting a just cause like this."

"I understand how you feel. No one wants to change things more than I do. But there's a right way and a wrong way to go about it. You've got to work within the system. . . ." Clare herself was dismayed at the clichés she heard coming out of her own mouth.

"What about my little girl? She's only four."

Clare cringed inwardly, thinking of her own children. "I'm sorry," Clare said, standing to indicate that the meeting was over.

"Okay, what's the point in begging?" said Ellen, wiping away her tears. "But you can tell Charlotte that she can fire me but she can't fire a whole movement."

Under ordinary circumstances Clare Henson enjoyed attending board meetings. It gave her a sense of power. This month, however, she was anxious and upset.

The board held its monthly meeting in an air-conditioned room on the twenty-first floor of the new building. Present were the director and deputy director of the hospital, the director of nursing and her deputy, Clare, and representatives from many of the medical and surgical services. The issue of nurses' notes made the day's discussion electric.

Dr. Stover, the hospital director, called for new business and recognized Clare. He was a stooped man who spoke with a Boston accent. When he wasn't carefully controlling it, his wide mouth hung open in a cadaverous grin.

"Several months ago," she began slowly, "I submitted a proposal entitled 'Nurses' Notes.' This proposal calls for a vote on a major policy change at this hospital." She paused. This was the big moment, which she had been planning and preparing for half a year. "This change will bring our hospital into the forefront of progressive institutions."

There were a few snickers from the bank of doctors opposite her.

"Exactly what are you proposing?" asked Dr. Irwin Greenberg, the head of gynecology. He was a heavyset man who perspired a lot in the July heat. Now, even in the air-conditioned boardroom, he was still patting his upper lip.

"Does anyone else need me to go over the proposal?" she asked, annoyed.

"I don't think that's necessary," said Dr. Stover after a pause. "I read it, and it was a very thorough and well-presented document."

"Hey," said Dr. Greenberg, laughing. "I didn't say I hadn't read it." He paused. "As a matter of fact, I haven't, but still that's no reason for you to jump to conclusions." Some other doctors thought this was funny. "To be very honest with you, Miss Henson, I'm just too busy saving lives to spend much time reading. I did skim it, though."

Dr. Mackey raised his hand, staring at Clare. "I think we should vote against this proposed change. I think it's wrong to integrate doctors' and nurses' comments. We doctors didn't go to school for fourteen years to have our comments put side by side with the nurses'! It would be too confusing. You wouldn't know what was what. That's quite a promotion you nurses are asking for!" He stared directly at Clare.

"The nurses would still have to sign their names and titles," said Clare calmly. "The problem is, as we all know, people now tend to ignore the nurses' comments. And that can be dangerous for the patients."

"I for one find the nurses' comments invaluable," said Ben Kendall, from the oncology department. "I'd like to see their inclusion in the general notes."

"That's nice, Kendall," said Dr. Mackey contemptuously. "Why don't you put on a skirt and join the rank-and-file nurses?"

"Wait just a minute!" said Ben furiously. "To begin with, not all nurses are women, Dr. Mackey. You're just trying to divert attention from the real issues being raised here about the status of nurses." Clare had never seen him so angry.

"I guess you didn't see the latest leaflet where they called our friend Charlotte a monster?" Mackey thundered.

"Don't worry about my feelings," Charlotte said sweetly. "What's important is the reputation of this hospital. My department is taking steps to make sure this won't happen again."

Clare, in a desperate attempt to salvage her proposal, said, "Let's remember it's patients' lives we're concerned with here. And my proposal is an important safeguard."

Ben Kendall said, "I think this proposal will forestall morale problems down the road. I would suggest we vote for it."

Dr. Merrill, a beefy-faced surgeon, said, "Let's just vote this proposal down and show we can't be pushed around."

"I'm not so sure that's a good idea," said Dr. Stover quietly. "I've seen the leaflet. Of course, we are all disturbed by these vicious attacks on staff members. However, it is important to remember the patients. I for one never really thought about how important this issue is, but we shouldn't vote in an emotionally charged atmosphere."

"Hear! Hear!" said Mackey. "My point exactly. This is a one-sided document."

"What do you mean?" asked Clare, her face coloring.

"It's a radical position paper."

"Dr. Mackey, I do present both sides of the issue," said Clare. "I think I'm favoring the Riverview Hospital position."

"In the light of all this acrimony, don't you think we should put this off for further discussion?" asked Charlotte.

"I volunteer to draw up an equal and opposite paper," said Mackey, as if by prearrangement. "The board needs more time to think."

Greenberg made the motion and it was carried. Dr. Stover adjourned the meeting.

In the hallway Clare pulled Ben Kendall aside. "Thank you," she said.

"It's so infuriating that they put off the vote," Ben said.

"On the contrary," Clare said, smiling grimly. "If they had voted today, Ben, we would have lost by a landslide."

In the stairwell Philip Mackey was talking with Charlotte.

"I can't thank you enough, Philip," she said flirtatiously. "We should stick together more often. We make quite a team."

"I'm certainly glad nobody brought up that nonsense from the other day," said Mackey. "I thought for sure your girl Clare was going to accuse me of being a mass murderer any minute."

"Philip, I don't think you have anything to worry about. I've taken care of everything."

"What do you mean?"

"That young nurse with the bad attitude"—she paused for effect—"was caught leafletting."

"I told you she had a bad attitude," he said triumphantly.

"And the best part is I made Clare Henson fire her," said Charlotte.

"Brilliant move, Charlotte!" boomed Mackey. "My only regret is that I couldn't have been there to watch her doing it."

Toward the end of July Karen agreed to meet Joan for dinner in the cafeteria. She had skipped lunch to take care of

Mrs. Bloom, who was running a fever. Now she was starved. She made her way from the new building to the Astor Pavilion through a warm summer shower.

At the entrance to Astor, a nurse with an umbrella handed her a soggy leaflet. "You're Miss Bovit, aren't you?" she asked.

Karen was startled. She peered under the umbrella and recognized Jill Curtis from the recovery room.

"How are you getting along?" Jill asked in a friendly way.

"Fine," said Karen. She glanced at the leaflet. "What's this all about?"

"Read it and see," said Jill, who leaned over to hand leaflets to two male nurses.

Karen read:

# A GOOD NURSE IS FIRED

Last week Ellen Garrison, a nurse on Astor Ten, was fired by Clare Henson, associate director of nursing. There is no doubt, however, who was really behind this firing: Charlotte Morgan, director of nursing, and Dr. Philip Mackey, head of anesthesia.

The official charge was "theft of hospital property." The property in question: a few pieces of paper. What was really involved here was something else. Ellen had charged Mackey with endangering a patient's life by failing to read the nurses' notes.

So naturally, the doctor got off scot-free, while the accusing nurse was fired!

How long are nurses going to put up with this situation, in which we have no rights and can be fired for trivial causes when we speak up on behalf of our patients?

Come to our next meeting at the Friends Meeting Hall

to see what we nurses can do to improve conditions for patients at Riverview Hospital.

—RANK-AND-FILE NURSES

"Will you come to our meeting?" Jill asked.

Karen was excited, yet a bit frightened. "Well, I'll try to," she said. "I'd certainly like to know more. How's Ellen doing?"

"Not so good. They turned down her request for reinstatement. She's working per diem with a staffing agency, but that's no life. Ellen sent her daughter to live with her grandmother for the summer, while she looks for a full-time job."

Karen glanced at her watch: she was already a few minutes late for her dinner. She said good-bye and hurried into the hospital.

Joan hadn't shown up, however. After fifteen minutes Karen decided to go to her instead. She vividly imagined Joan in the SICU break room lost in gossip. When she got to SICU she found Joan hard at work on a patient. The man's respirator had a very loud alarm and she was yelling at Sarah, "Damn it! Turn that thing off!"

She glanced up, saw Karen, but turned back to her work, removing a blood-soaked piece of gauze from the patient and replacing it with a clean one. Karen silently watched her friend in admiration. Joan was a topflight nurse.

Joan washed up and came over. "Hi," she said, puzzled at first. "Oh, I forgot our dinner. This guy's a bleeder. Sorry."

"Don't be silly," said Karen. "I can come back some other time."

"No, he's fine for now. Bijan pumped him full of antihemophilic factor."

They went to the cafeteria and took trays of chow mein to their table. "So what's new with you?" asked Joan, taking a bite.

"Nothing much," said Karen. "Oh, I got a postcard from Eric Sadler. Remember Eric?"

"Sure. Dr. Berg's gunshot wound. He was that handsome kid who had a crush on you," said Joan. "Or maybe it was the other way around?"

Karen blushed. "I don't know where you get your information," she said. "Anyway, great news. He graduated from high school. And now he's recuperating in the mountains. Dr. Berg says he's going to correct the colostomy next month. He wants me to be his nurse. Hopefully, Mrs. Bloom's complications will be resolved by then."

"There's one lucky kid," said Joan, with a mouth full of food. "You read about that type all the time—he's lucky to be alive."

"By the way, have you seen this?" Karen asked, handing her the leaflet.

Joan scanned it quickly. "A bunch of crap, as usual," she said, and handed it back. "I knew Ellen. She was trouble from the git-go."

"Did Clare tell you what happened at the board meeting?" Karen asked.

"Clare, and Mackey too. She called me that night to pour out her soul. I don't take sides between friends."

Karen winced. "I didn't speak to Dr. Mackey, of course," she said with a touch of sarcasm, "but I did speak to Clare. Frankly, I think your friend Dr. Mackey is sabotaging her proposal."

"Karen, you don't even work here. What are you getting involved for?"

"I am a nurse," Karen said. "So it affects me. I'm

thinking of going to the rank-and-file nurses' next meeting," she ventured.

Joan smiled. "Oh, I can't wait to hear Clare's excuses when she blackballs you from the hospital! 'This hurts me more than it hurts you,'" Joan said, mimicking Clare.

Karen said, "I seriously doubt I would be blackballed from Riverview for attending a meeting."

Joan wiped her mouth. "Come on, walk me back to the unit," she said. "What's the difference!" she said, laughing inappropriately. If Karen hadn't known better she would have thought Joan was high.

As they got to the elevators the doors opened and a heavy nurse pushed out a gurney holding an unconscious patient. She spotted Joan. "Okay, this is our last transfer of the day, and thank God. If you need any floating staff, Joanie, you just let me know after we dump this meat. . . ."

"Well, there you are—the professional nurse of today!" Joan said triumphantly.

# FOUR

## August

Eric Sadler returned to Riverview in August to have his colostomy reversed. Despite his absence he had won the history award at graduation. In just a few weeks he would enter the state university. Karen informed the Blooms that they no longer needed her. Actually, they seemed a bit relieved, because they realized Mrs. Bloom could be in the hospital for a long time, and costs were mounting.

She was now free to take care of Eric for a couple of weeks. Everything went well until it came time for Eic to leave the hospital. He insisted that he needed Karen at home to nurse him. His parents were more than willing to pay. When she refused, he acted hurt.

"Eric, you have to understand," Karen said. "I am not abandoning you. You just don't need one-to-one nursing care anymore. There's a difference between abandoning a person and finishing a job."

"That's all I am, a job?" Eric asked petulantly.

"Don't be ridiculous," Karen said, sighing. "We've

worked hard to complete a nursing care plan that would lead to your independence. Now it's time to let go."

"Am I asking you to stay forever? No," he answered himself. "Just for another week or so. Why can't you stay till then?"

Karen smiled kindly. "The whole point is for you to develop your independence. It has to start sometime, and now's the time. Believe me, Eric, you'll feel more confident going to college after having been on your own for a month."

"Look, Karen," Eric said in a pleading tone. "Please don't make me beg for your company. This is hard for me to say. But I need to be with you."

"I like to be with you too," she said. She knew that it was different. Over the past few months Eric had clearly developed and maintained a crush on her. At first it had been flattering, and she realized she might have even encouraged it. Now it worried her. "Eric," she said, "you know I enjoy your company. I really do." Her voice was low. "You're a really nice guy. And I think you've done incredibly well in adjusting to all these changes that you've had to face. But everything comes to an end."

"You sound like a funeral director," Eric said, laughing. He sat down opposite her. "Karen, let's face it. You're not just my nurse. I've explained how I feel about you." He stared hard at her. "What about the graduation card you sent me? Didn't you sign it 'Love always'?"

It was Karen's turn to laugh. "Eric, what do you want me to say? You're putting me in an impossible situation."

"Okay," he said with a new idea. "Let's just forget about your being my nurse. That's finished. Now I'd like to ask you out. In fact, I'd like to invite you up to my parents' place in the country for a week. Would you come?"

She smiled. "I'd love to," she said gently, "but I'm afraid that's impossible."

"I know you're a little older than me. I'm eighteen years old. Plenty of couples have met in the hospital just like this, haven't they?"

She stared at him and tried not to smile. "You know I like you, Eric," she said. "More importantly, I think I have helped you recuperate from your gunshot. I've done my job the best way I know how. I'm simply not looking for another kind of relationship right now, Eric. If you got the idea that there was more to it than that, I'm sorry. I really am."

Eric sighed and stood up. With his shoulders hunched over, he leaned against the window. "You led me on, Karen," he said bitterly. "What about the card?" he asked.

"That was just a way I sign my cards." It was time to get a bit tougher, she thought. "Look, Eric, today's Friday. I'm going to take the weekend off. On Monday I intend to start a new case," she said pointedly.

Suddenly the door opened. It was Clare, in her clean white lab coat, clipboard in hand. "Oh, excuse me! I hope I'm not interrupting anything." Eric stared at Clare without saying anything. "Karen, do you think I could see you at the nurses' station when you're done?" She smiled at Eric, asked how he was feeling, and left after getting the expected answer. The break relieved some of the tension, however.

"Let's both calm down. I guess it's never easy to say good-bye," Karen said.

"You just don't realize how much I'm going to miss you," Eric said, his voice breaking.

Karen walked over, hugged him, and said, "Good-bye, Eric." She quickly broke free from his embrace. She felt relieved as she walked out and found Clare waiting for her at the nurses' station.

Clare was studying Eric's chart. "Karen, I hate to keep you overtime, but let's just talk for a couple of minutes."

"Sure, anything wrong? Let me make a summary note for today," she said, taking the chart from Clare.

"So how's it going?" Clare asked informally.

"Great," said Karen. "You know, I've even been thinking of dropping Dr. Berg a note, thanking him for getting me started at Riverview."

"How's Eric's mental state?"

"He's okay. Suffering some separation anxiety. He's a little confused about our relationship, but on the whole he's doing well."

"I was quite surprised by one thing I read in his chart."

"What's that?" asked Karen.

"Fourteen days is a long time to work without a day off, Karen. I mean, dedication is one thing, but this is ridiculous. Don't you need some time off for your own life?"

Karen laughed uneasily. "Well, I'd think you'd be glad I take my work so seriously."

"Well, that depends on what you mean by 'seriously,' " Clare said. "It's important to get away from the hospital sometimes. You know, the other day Joan reminded me how Miss Parker lectured you about just this kind of thing."

Karen blushed. "Miss Parker could be so mean! That was one of the most embarrassing moments of my life."

"If I remember correctly, you developed an infatuation for one of your patients. Miss Parker let you have it in front of the whole class."

"And leave it to you to bring this up ten years later!" Karen said, laughing.

Clare was laughing too. Underneath it, however, she was serious. "Karen, the point is this"—she paused—"are you nursing your patients or are they nursing you?"

* * *

Heather Asher lay in a corner of the Surgical Intensive Care Unit. The lighting was subdued, the silence punctuated only by the beep of monitors. Heather was no longer the tanned, vivacious woman who had enjoyed sailing off the coast of Spain. Now she looked old and frail as she lay unconscious.

"A Whipple," Laura, the day nurse, said to Joan, shaking her head. Laura was a woman about Joan's age, tall, with a pale flat face and a mop of dirty blond curls.

"What's that again?" asked Joan. "I remember the name from school, but I don't think I've ever seen one."

"That's because they hardly do them anymore. And with good reason."

"What exactly is it?" asked Joan, intrigued.

"It's the last resort for pancreatic cancer," said Laura.

Joan winced. "Christ, pancreatic CA. That's the worst." She shuddered. "Why do they even bother operating? I mean, they can't do anything for her. What do they get—five percent remissions?"

"It's pretty grim. Basically, they go in and take out everything they can. And then they call it 'heroic surgery,'" said Laura with a touch of bitterness. "Heroic referring to the doctors, of course, not the patients."

"Unbelievable," said Joan. "The poor woman. Well, in a way, it's a challenge for us," said Joan. "We'll see if we can keep her alive and prevent complications."

"Take care," said Laura. "I'm off on a long weekend. And believe me, I need it."

Sarah approached. "Joan, do you want to draw Asher's blood? They'll be coming for it in about fifteen minutes."

Joan carefully cleared various lines and drains out of the way and lifted up Heather's limp arm. "Give me a chuck to put under here," she said. Sarah passed her a square of blue plastic. Joan put a tourniquet on the upper arm and pulled down the examining light as her eyes and fingers searched for an available vein.

"You know, this is strange," said Sarah, studying the chart. "Her potassium level has been dropping since the operation."

"You're kidding," said Joan. She found a vein on her third attempt and inserted the syringe. "Didn't anybody notice that? What's in the IV?"

"Five percent dextrose, one quarter normal saline, with twenty-milli-equivalents of potassium," said Sarah.

"Nothing unusual there. Okay," Joan said, handing Sarah three test tubes of blood, "let's see how these come back. In the meantime, let's put her on a continuous CVP monitor."

Sarah attached the central venous pressure monitor to the catheter extending all the way into the heart. Joan went to page the resident. She studied the numbers in the chart, her brow wrinkled. "Listen, Sarah," she said, "do me a favor . . ."

"Why do I love to hear those words?" asked Sarah, sighing.

"I'm going to do total care for Asher and I would like you to deal with any problems that come up in the unit."

"No problem," said Sarah, "but I expect your paycheck this week."

"You can have my whole frigging job," said Joan.

"Your horoscope says you're going to marry a rich man," said Sarah, laughing.

"I'll have to tell that one to Phil Mackey tonight," said Joan, without looking up.

Bijan came hurrying in, a stethoscope dangling out of his pocket. No matter how rushed, he always had a pleasant manner.

"What took you so long?" asked Joan playfully. She liked to abuse him.

"Same charming Joan," he said, undaunted. "What's up?" He glanced over at Heather. "I hate to say it," he whispered, "but she doesn't look too good."

"Save your comments and just take a look at the monitor," said Joan, pursing her lips.

"Why the irregular heartbeats, I wonder?" Bijan said to himself. The screen showed an occasionally wild phosphorescent green blip. "Probably nothing serious. If they start to come more frequently, then we could be in for a lot of trouble. Let me see the latest test results." Joan handed him the chart.

"White blood count normal, hemoglobin . . ."

"Look at the potassium," she interrupted.

He smiled in a good-natured way. "I was just about to say, the potassium seems a bit low. That could certainly cause irregular beats."

"A bit low?" She raised her eyebrows.

He laughed delightedly.

"Bijan, order some more K for her," said Joan.

"Maybe. First I want some fresh blood samples."

"Done," said Joan. "Sent them down about fifteen minutes ago."

The blips continued. "Okay, let's go top to bottom and check the lines," he said. "Something might have come loose."

Joan pulled the sheet down from Heather's small body. She and Bijan stood on opposite sides of the bed. There were lines and tubes coming out everywhere.

"Nasogastric tube is draining bloody mucus," she said.

"That's okay. Is she on hourly intake and output?" asked the resident.

"Oh, give me a break," Joan said. "We've been watching her like a hawk."

Sarah brought over the latest lab results. "Bad news! Her potassium's now 2.2."

Bijan looked at Joan and said quietly, "That *is* bad. We could be in deep trouble if this keeps up."

"The subclavian CVP line is in place and functioning," she continued. "The patient is on a respirator, but breathing on her own."

"Is the alarm on?" he asked.

Joan nodded. "We've got three EKG leads in place. Aside from the occasional premature ventricular contractions, she's in normal sinus rhythm."

"Let's give her another bolus dose of potassium," said Bijan. He watched for a minute, then went across the room to check on another patient.

Joan administered the additional potassium. Heather's heart should have responded to the drug—if her problem was indeed caused by a lack of potassium—but it didn't. In fact, there was an increase in the number of heartbeat irregularities. "I don't know what the hell is going on," Joan said to Sarah. "I think we may be losing her." She was wondering what to do about Heather's husband, who was staring into the unit, when the cardiac alarm suddenly went off. "Bijan!" she screamed. He had heard it and was on his way.

Joan quickly shut off the alarm on the monitor and looked at him. This was it. Bijan said, "You know, I don't think the potassium has anything to do with this! But I'll be damned if I know . . . Sometimes the catheter will irritate the heart." He thought for a moment. "I'm going to pull the central line," he said. It was a tricky move, but the woman was sinking. Joan quickly set up a sterile field, and the resident pulled the Swan-Ganz catheter out of Heather Asher's heart as gently as he could.

Joan and Bijan stood on opposite sides of the bed, their own hearts racing, waiting to see if this last desperate attempt would have any effect at all.

"It's working!" Bijan suddenly exclaimed. The monitor now showed a steady stabilization of Heather's heartbeat.

"Nice moves," Joan said to him in a low voice.

Bijan stood for a minute quietly looking at the screen, then smiled, crossed his fingers, and walked away.

Joan worked for a while at Heather's bedside before she realized someone was watching her. A silver-haired man paced back and forth in the small visitors' area, stopped to stare, and then paced again.

"Oh, my God," she said to Sarah, who was working at the bed next to Heather's. "I forgot all about him!"

"Who?" asked Sarah without looking up.

"The husband," said Joan. "Darn! I should have remembered. I saw him out there earlier and then I forgot all about him." She was still feeling all charged up.

"I'll stand in for you here while you talk to him," said Sarah.

"Okay," said Joan. "We've got Heather all squared away." She checked the monitor. "The potassium's okay and her heartbeat's strong and steady. That was a close call. Just keep a lookout and I'll be back in a few minutes."

Joan greeted Norton Asher and took him into the break room. He was an attractive, athletic-looking man of about sixty. "I'm sorry I couldn't get away sooner. My name is Joan Fisher. I'm the head nurse on evenings."

"I've been watching you working on my wife," Norton said. "Is there anything wrong?"

"She's fine. Would you like some coffee?"

"I didn't want to disturb you," he said. "Is she still yellow?"

"I'm afraid so," said Joan. "The jaundice won't clear up for a while." She poured two cups from a standing pot. "So how did you come to Riverview?" asked Joan, in an attempt to break the ice.

"Well, to make a long story short," he said, leaning forward, "Heather and I were sailing off the coast of Spain when she turned yellow."

"That must have been frightening."

"It really was. At the time we thought it was the shellfish or something."

Joan sipped her coffee, settling into her chair. Norton also relaxed.

"We took the first flight out to London. The doctor who examined her told us it might be—" He paused at the word and took a sip of the murky liquid.

"—cancer," Joan finished.

"He recommended surgery, immediate and extensive surgery, and so we figured we had better head straight back to America."

"Where are you from?" Joan asked.

"Nowhere." He laughed. "We live on our boat, the *Bluebonnet*."

Joan smiled broadly. "God, that sounds romantic!"

"It's great," Norton said with conviction. "Of course, I could tell you about the tangled anchors and the near collisions. But we love it. It's such a healthy life." He paused to sip his coffee. "Which is why it's so hard for me to believe Heather is sick. It's unreal."

"It must be difficult," said Joan.

"She's not the kind of woman who can stay in bed very long. She's just a bundle of energy. You're going to have your hands full when she wakes up."

Joan smiled kindly. It wasn't at all certain that the unconscious woman would ever wake up again, but she had seen stranger things happen.

"Heather's a remarkable woman. She became a sailor late in life. You'd never know it to watch her in action, though. She's a natural. I can't wait till we get back to it."

"How did you get started sailing?" Joan asked, intrigued.

"I sold my business and retired early. It was Heather's idea originally." He closed his eyes and thought for a moment.

"How big a boat is it?" she asked.

"We started out with a twenty-four-foot sailer-cruiser. It cost us six thousand dollars. You know, she said a funny thing at the time. She said, 'Norton, I feel like I have one of those rare tropical diseases. The kind that lays dormant for years and then suddenly breaks out.' I said, 'What are you talking about?' and she said, 'Sailing. I gotta have a boat!' I guess you could call it a whim. But she was serious. We got books and charts and we studied them. We sold our house in Laguna and took off."

"That's wonderful," said Joan. "What a great life."

He looked around the room. "I can't wait to go back to it."

Sarah came to the lounge. "You'll excuse me, Mr. Asher," said Joan. "My own crew is about to mutiny. You can come in in about fifteen minutes, if you like, and see your wife."

Norton nodded. "In a minute." He closed his eyes. Joan was surprised to see a faint smile on his face. He was probably thinking something pleasant about Heather and the *Bluebonnet*.

# FIVE

## September

The Friends Meeting Hall was a tall brick building not far
from the hospital. In the lobby was a black and white
directory, and Karen found the entry that said RANK AND
FILE. The porter directed her to a bare second-floor room that
echoed with laughing sounds within.

She was a few minutes late, and the room was already
practically filled with people. In the back, Karen saw a little
girl sitting by a table with homemade cakes, a new stack of
leaflets, and a coffee urn. Karen took a cup.

"Are you a friend of my mommy?" asked the girl.

"Who's your mommy?" asked Karen, smiling.

The girl pointed shyly to Ellen Garrison, who waved
from the back row.

Karen whispered, "Yes, I am," and stuck a dollar into a
coffee can labeled DONATIONS. She took a seat.

Jill Curtis was at the podium, chairing the meeting. She
had her glasses on and looked as studious and self-
possessed as she did at work. "The real question," she was
saying, "is where do we go from here? So far, the rank-and-

file movement has grown, as this meeting shows. But where are we going? We need to define our goals."

"Now you're talking!" It was Sarah from the SICU. "All this name-calling isn't going to get us anywhere. We have to do something." She sat down. There was some heavy self-conscious applause at this.

"What we do depends on what the board does," said Ellen. Karen admired her for staying involved after losing her job at Riverview.

"Exactly. So why don't we hear from the one person here who really understands the thinking of the board," said Jill. She had a cat-that-swallowed-the-canary look.

Karen was surprised when she saw a handsome doctor stand up in the front row and walk, tentatively, to the podium. She had often seen him around the hospital. "I'm Dr. Kendall, oncology," he said. "I'm also a member of the hospital board." He paused. Karen shared the electric excitement. Everyone knew this was treason to the doctors' fraternity.

"I'm here because I believe in integrated notes," he began. There was loud applause at this, which he waved off, modestly. "At the board meeting, Dr. Philip Mackey—" He was cut off by hisses and boos, then "shushes," and tittering laughter. He continued. "Dr. Mackey made a presentation in opposition to Clare Henson's proposal for integrated notes. In fact," he said, his voice rising, "the Henson report should have been passed this summer."

"You said it!" Sarah exclaimed.

"What did the board decide?" Jill interjected in a businesslike way.

"Well, the vote was put off for two months."

"Oh no!" said Ellen. "That sounds like them." There was a lot of derisive laughter, but people were angry.

"The current plan is to vote at the November meeting," said Ben.

"In that case, I suggest we also have a plan for November," said Ellen. "And my plan is this: let's shut down the hospital, if that's what it takes to get justice around here." There was loud applause. Karen clapped politely, too, but found Ellen's bitterness a bit frightening.

"What do you mean, shut down?" shouted someone. "A strike?"

"Whatever it takes," said Sarah.

"I won't have anything to do with a strike. That hurts the patients."

"Come on!"

The crowd bickered for a few more minutes. Finally Jill took control and said, "Listen, everybody! Let's set up an informational picket line outside the hospital on the day of the board meeting."

"I saw once on TV nurses dressed up like doctors to make their point. And it worked! We could do the same thing—all wear lab coats and suits." There was appreciative laughter at this.

"Great idea! We could get a lot of media coverage for that," said a large nurse from the emergency room. "My brother's a cameraman. I know some of the reporters."

"I think it's a great idea!" said Ellen. "Let the public find out what's really happening at Riverview."

"What day did you say that was?" Jill asked.

"The twenty-first of November," said Ben, checking his calendar.

"November twenty-first," Sarah repeated, smiling. "That's just before Thanksgiving. Don't be a turkey," she said.

Jill's idea was formulated as a motion and passed unanimously.

\* \* \*

In the hallway, Karen ran into Sarah.

"Ready to march and inform?" Sarah asked, laughing.

Karen's adrenaline was still pumping from the meeting. She had never been to anything like this before. "Sure. Let's hope the board doesn't change the date," she responded.

"Aren't you Joan's friend?" Sarah asked, more seriously.

"Yes, I am," said Karen, looking through the departing crowd. She was hoping Ben might talk to her.

"Do you think we could go somewhere for a minute?" Sarah took her arm and steered her away from the hubbub. "Why don't you talk to Joan?" Sarah began. "I've tried, but I'm getting nowhere."

Karen was puzzled. "About what?"

"Her drinking, that's what."

"What do you mean?" said Karen defensively.

"She's always hung over, in case you haven't noticed. I wouldn't say this to anyone else, but she might even be drinking on the job," she said gently.

Karen pondered this. "I've seen her at work in the unit. She seemed fine. Work hard, play hard—that's Joan's philosophy." Karen couldn't believe Joan was drinking on the job.

"Okay," said Sarah, turning away sadly. "I hope you're right and I'm wrong."

The following week, Karen arrived at Riverview to begin a new case. She had slept practically all weekend, only going out in the sweltering heat to see a foreign film on Third Avenue with Joan. Waiting for a coffee at the wagon, she ran into Jill, who was going off duty.

"Stay and chat for a few minutes," Karen said.

"I'm going home," said Jill. "I just got rotated to nights

for two weeks and I'm dying already. The only thing I want to talk about is sleep!"

"Have a good day's sleep," said Karen. On the eleventh floor, she went looking for her new patient, Roxanne Warfield. From the sight of all the cradles and trapezes she knew it would be an orthopedic case. When she found the nursing station it was in an uproar. A red-faced nurse was yelling at a physician: "Dr. Tyson! You've got to transfer her to psych. I'm speaking for everyone on the floor. We simply can't deal with her!"

Tyson was a small, well-dressed man, every strand of his silver hair neatly in place. He held up his hand in a gesture of silence. It worked. "Please, be patient!" Dr. Tyson said. "She has flatly refused to see a psychiatrist. The hospital has hired private nurses around the clock to alleviate some of the burden on the staff." There was a murmur of approval.

"Psychiatric nurses, I hope?" asked an aide.

"Competent nurses," said Tyson forcefully. "I assure you, as soon as is practical we'll have her out of the hospital. I don't want our routine disrupted any more than it is already."

"Excuse me," said Karen, approaching a staff nurse. "Could you tell me what room Roxanne Warfield is in?"

A slow, malicious smile spread across the nurse's face. Karen heard an aide say, "All *right!*" and laugh.

"I hope you're a psychiatric nurse," she said sweetly, in a way that only increased Karen's anxiety.

"Why?" asked Karen.

"Karen Bovit?" said a woman behind her, who had been listening in. "I'm Audrey Dana. Come on. I'll give you orientation as we walk," she said. "Roxanne's in 1104. Just come and see me at lunchtime if you can't handle her."

They chatted about the floor makeup, and Karen liked

Audrey's no-nonsense approach. A few steps before the door, Audrey turned around and waved good-bye. Taking a deep breath, Karen walked in.

On the bed was a woman in her late twenties. Her hair was curly. Her face was full, a double chin showing above her pajamas. Her oval green eyes were clever, almost sly-looking. Roxanne's bed was equipped with an orthopedic trapeze and her knee was in a cast and elevated by a sling. She squinted up at Karen.

"Well, I don't believe it! You're white! Wait, let me pinch myself. I must be dreaming."

Karen's mouth fell open.

"Oh, I get it. You're a deaf mute! That's great."

Karen was shocked and wary. "I feel the need to introduce some formality into this relationship," she said stiffly. "My name is Karen Bovit. You will address me as Nurse Bovit and I will address you as Patient Warfield."

Roxanne was curious. She cocked her head to one side and asked, "Why is that, may I ask?"

"Because I'm insecure," Karen said coolly. She said this with a perfectly straight face, but Roxanne laughed—a loud, spontaneous laugh.

"Okay, then, *Nurse Bovit*," she said, her voice laced with sarcasm, "would you do me a favor, and go back out to the nurses' station and tell Dr. Tyson that I want to see him? Alone."

Karen studied the mischievous, animated look on Roxanne's face. For fun she saluted. Roxanne saluted in return. Karen made her way out of the room. Dr. Tyson was not at the nurses' station. She looked and found him by the stairwell chatting with two residents.

"Hello, Dr. Tyson," she said amiably. "I'm Karen Bovit, the private nurse for Roxanne Warfield. She would like to see you alone, if you don't mind."

"Here we go again," said Tyson, and the residents smiled and shook their heads in sympathy. When they got to the room he turned and said, "Nurse, sorry, what did you say your name was? Karen? Why don't you come in with me? You'll find this very instructive."

"If it's all right with Roxanne," said Karen. "She did say 'alone.' "

Dr. Tyson looked at her as if she were from another planet. "Well, I say you can be there," he said. When they entered, Roxanne's eyes were shining, her mouth curved upward in a manic grin, and her whole face glowed with excitement. When she spoke, however, her voice came out in a surprisingly subdued tone.

"Dr. Tyson, you and I go way back together. And in your heart you know that I don't want to sue this piece of rat shit you call a hospital. But what choice do I have?" she pleaded.

"Not to sue," said Tyson.

"Look, Dr. Tyson," she said, her voice rising now, "you have exposed me to a criminally negligent crew of malicious asswipes!"

"Roxanne—" Tyson began.

"And because I uncovered their criminal actitivies you have the nerve to call in a shrink on me."

"Roxanne, I only suggested you might want to see a psychiatrist," Dr. Tyson said patiently.

"You know what I say to that?" she screamed. The swollen veins were standing out on her neck now. "I say," she whispered, and then shrieked, "fuck that shit!" She winced, as if she were getting a headache from the effort.

"A psychiatric workup could be very enlightening."

"I'll see you in court."

"I'm really worried," he said sarcastically. He got up to

leave but paused at the door. "Do you want to tell me your version of what happened this morning?"

She settled back on her pillows. "All right, at last someone wants to hear. At six-thirty this morning your own orthopedic resident—"

"Which one?" asked Tyson.

"The queer little Bible thumper," said Roxanne. "Dr. Dial-a-Prayer. He came in to examine my knee. And when he was finished I begged him for some analgesic drugs. Does that make me crazy?"

"And then?" Tyson said impatiently.

"Listen the fuck up! Next he knocked over a stack of plastic cups sitting on my bedside there"—she gestured— "and they hit the floor. Then this Bible freak had the nerve to *pick them up* and put them where I could drink from them."

"And?" asked Tyson, closing his eyes.

"And! And!! And you must think I'm awfully stupid. Where the fuck did he go to medical school, anyway? Armageddon U.? Come on, Tyson, you don't have to be Einfuckingstein to know you throw away cups that have fallen on the floor."

"Come on, Roxanne," said Tyson. "All this commotion over just a few paper cups?" He picked them up and chucked them in the garbage. "There."

"Destroying evidence!" she screamed. "Look, Tyson, we're paying you top dollar and what do I get? Some second-string, second-rate faggot examining me, when what I want is the mother-fucking-superior!"

"That's it!" said Tyson angrily. "I've had about enough of you, Roxanne. Your parents are making such a sacrifice to get you the best care. I think you should be making an equal effort to get out of here as quickly as you can." He turned to leave.

Suddenly Roxanne burst into a violent storm of tears. She thrashed her head this way and that—her motions were severely limited by her bandaged leg in the sling. "If I were you, I'd get the best lawyer money can buy, you dickless wonder," she yelled at the doctor as he retreated. Then in a tiny voice she said to Karen, "Nurse Bovit . . . don't listen to what they say about me, okay?" Karen saluted and followed the doctor out.

"I'm in pain!" they could hear Roxanne yelling from inside. "I want my frigging medicine!" An elderly patient, pushing a walker in front of him, looked at them, astonished.

"What was *that* all about?" Karen asked.

"Well, now you've seen Roxanne in action, our resident loudmouth," said Dr. Tyson. He was agitated but tried not to show it. "Do you still want to stay with the case? Karen, you seem to have some sort of unusual rapport with her. I could sense it. The nurses at Riverview are able to handle Roxanne, of course, but she takes too much time away from the other patients."

"She seems awfully angry," said Karen. "What's her story?"

"About ten years ago she was in a serious ski accident. She went down the expert slope after just one or two lessons, which is typical of her. One knee came right out of the socket and she tore up all the cartilage in the other. We did the best we could for her in those days, but she missed a lot of school. She became angry all the time. There must have been some underlying mental condition. I feel very sorry for her, but what she needs now is a psychiatrist." A piercing beeper went off in his pocket and he glanced at his watch. "Combined staff meeting," he said. "Got to go. Good luck. Let me know if I can help." And he was gone.

Karen returned uncertainly to her patient. "Oh, hi there," said Roxanne calmly.

Karen walked over to the bed. "Anything I can get you?" she asked.

"As a matter of fact, there is," Roxanne said in an off-the-cuff manner. "Do you think you could negotiate my Demerol shot for me?"

Karen picked up the chart from the foot of the bed. "It's not time yet, Roxanne. You just had a shot three hours ago."

"Bend the rules a little, for godsake. I'm in serious pain here." She winced unconvincingly.

"Well," said Karen, smiling, "I'm afraid there are laws about that. It's much better for you to adhere strictly to the pain relief regimen."

"Let me see that chart," Roxanne said.

"Sure," said Karen, handing it to Roxanne. She was not about to deny Roxanne's request to see her care plan.

"You're a great bullshit artist," said Roxanne, but without the usual vehemence. "Look, Karen, let's be friends. Let's cooperate." She handed the chart back, having barely glanced at it.

"Fine," said Karen noncommittally.

"Relax. I'm not trying to get you to do anything illegal. It's just that these fucking narcotics nurses, with their keys to the kingdom, sometimes take forever in opening up the box. *Capisce?*"

"I'll tell you what," said Karen. "I'll go sign the drugs out, but you can't have them until it's time. Okay?"

"Sounds good to me," said Roxanne. "You can hold up the vial and get your rocks off while I writhe in pain waiting for it."

Karen went to the station and found Audrey, who had the

narcotics keys. She had just finished rounds and was washing her hands.

"You know, Karen," she said, "I think I speak for the entire floor when I beg you on bended knee to stick with Roxanne."

"As a general rule, I do not speak disparagingly about my patients," said Karen, smiling. "This case is an exception. I've never heard so much filthy language in my life!"

"Her mouth should be washed out with pHisohex," said Audrey angrily. "Four operations in three years, and we've had her every time. She deliberately screws up her knee so she'll wind up back here."

"That seems a bit extreme," said Karen.

"Oh yeah?" said Audrey. "Talk to me in a couple of weeks."

"Do you think that maybe she has a drug problem?" asked Karen tentatively. "She's begging me for medication, but she doesn't really seem to be in pain."

Audrey laughed in surprise. "Drug problem? What ever gave you that idea? She's Dr. Tyson's junkie, that's all!" Karen finished signing the narcotic book and handed it to Audrey for countersigning. Audrey opened the double-locked cabinet.

Cautiously, Karen asked, "What do you mean by 'Dr. Tyson's junkie'? Do you mean her need for drugs or her need for Dr. Tyson?"

Audrey handed her the Demerol. "Both," said Audrey.

"Thanks," said Karen. "I get the feeling you understand this situation better than anyone."

Audrey seemed flattered by Karen's attention. "She feels that every other doctor in the place has abandoned her," she confided.

"Yet she abuses him," said Karen.

"What can she do? Roxanne's a prescription junkie of the first order. For years Tyson's tried to get her to see a psychiatrist. Her problem's not his fault, despite what she says. The man's an outstanding ortho surgeon," she said. "We all like him a lot. And when it comes to Roxanne, he's got the patience of Job. Too much, if you ask me."

"Well, thanks for the hen session," said Karen, glancing at her watch. "Don't worry, I'll keep it under my hat."

Roxanne awoke from a doze when Karen entered. "Oh, there you are!" she said, rubbing her eyes. "I thought you were tying off with my medicine in the bathroom! God, I'm in agony! I must have fucking fainted from the pain!"

"Sure," said Karen, smiling without warmth. She gave Roxanne her shot and she lay back, sighing contentedly.

"You realize, of course, that Dr. Tyson is undermedicating me."

"What makes you think so?" asked Karen.

"To punish me for refusing to see a shrink. They think that just because I called a lawyer I need a psychiatrist."

"Do you really believe that?" Karen asked gently.

"Look, this is war. And all's fair in love and war, right?"

"Wrong," said Karen. "Don't have a tantrum now. Just think about other possibilities."

In a Thai restaurant Karen was having dinner with Joan on her evening off. "I know Roxy from the old days," said Joan. "They used to park her in the SICU just to give the ortho staff a break. She's only being nice to you because she thinks she's got you wrapped around her little finger. Cross her and she'll turn vicious."

"I wouldn't call her nice," said Karen. "We have developed a kind of special relationship. She is so difficult to get through to, though. How's things in the unit?"

"Same old soup," said Joan. "One thing occurs to me. Sarah—you know Sarah?—I think she's involved with the leafletters."

Karen smiled but said nothing.

"The best case I've got," Joan said, "is a pancreatic CA. Heather Asher. She's a tough lady. Ben Kendall's going to take over the case as soon as she's transferred out of the unit."

Karen suddenly was interested. "Do you think she'll need a private nurse?"

"I don't know," said Joan. "I'll ask Mr. Asher."

"By the way, how well do you know Ben Kendall?" Karen asked. She couldn't hide the interest in her voice.

"Seems like a nice enough guy." Joan smiled. She was well tuned to Karen's nuances. "In fact, I thought maybe I'd ask him out myself."

For a moment Karen was almost taken in by this ploy. "Oh, give me a break, Joan," she said suddenly, laughing easily.

"This sounds like Nancy Nurse," said Joan.

"What do you mean by that?" asked Karen.

"In college we used to have fun," said Joan. "But lately, every time I ask you to go out for drinks and meet some guys, you wrinkle up your nose. All you ever want to do, Karen, is talk about your damn patients. There's more to life than just nursing, you know."

Karen was flustered. "I know that, Joan. You don't have to lecture me." Her tone of voice indicated the discussion was over.

Roxanne was out of her sling now and sitting on the edge of the bed. She was highly agitated when Karen came in. "You gotta be trifuckinglingual around here!"

"What happened, Patient Warfield?" Karen said, summoning up their joking relationship.

"Taco-face refused to answer my bell during the night. She hid the buzzer, then claimed she didn't understand what the hell I was talking about. Sure, I made the mistake of talking English."

"When you make ethnic slurs you make people angry for no good reason."

"Well, you're making me angry for no reason, and that's not your fucking job, Nurse Bovit."

"I still wish you wouldn't talk about people that way," said Karen coldly. "It demeans you more than them."

Roxanne ignored her. "You've probably heard that Candy-ass Tyson is resurrecting his old 'see a shrink' line of shit."

"Why is it 'shit'?" Karen interrupted. She had been looking for an opening like this for a long time.

"Oh, come off it, Nurse Bovit. You know how I feel about psychiatrists." She smiled and with her fingertips imitated a jazz drummer on the over-bed table. "They sit and make believe they're listening to you for a mere one hundred and thirty dollars every fifteen minutes. You know what I call psychiatrists, Nurse Bovit?"

"I can hardly wait to find out," said Karen.

"I call them slimeballs. Every one of those jerkoffs took up a valuable seat in medical school"—she was picking up speed—"only to go out in the free fucking market and sell their phony-ass 'concern' to unsuspecting victims."

"Roxanne," Karen said, "no one can ever accuse you of not taking a stand on psychiatrists. However, I still think it would be helpful in your case."

There was dead silence. Both Karen and Roxanne knew that an invisible line had been crossed. Karen had gotten her attention and it was the most genuine moment of communication they had had in weeks. Roxanne nodded, as if to say, "Continue."

"The way I see it," Karen said softly, "you have several specific things to deal with during this hospital stay. One of them is your knee. The other one is your anger. Nobody is perfect, Roxanne. Most people would benefit from just talking to a psychiatrist."

"How do you think a shrink could help me?" she asked. Her tone of voice was almost normal, but the atmosphere was potentially explosive.

"You have to cut down on drugs and eventually cut them out. You have to adjust to being well, after so many years of pain. Dr. Tyson will be seeing you less and less."

Roxanne looked as if she had been slapped. "It's Dr. Tyson's fucking fault," she said, "that I'm so addicted." It was the first that Karen had heard her admit that she had a drug problem. "If ol' Candy-ass had succeeded in fixing my knee the first time I wouldn't be so strung out now." Her voice trailed off.

"You know," Karen said sharply, "everyone in the hospital goes home, except you. You have to live in your body and with your body and with your anger all the time."

It rang true to Roxanne. She became uncharacteristically silent. "You know," she said finally, "I sure wish my parents could afford to keep paying you while I'm recuperating. They just can't afford it."

Karen was touched. "Why can't you just interview a few psychiatrists and find one that interests you?"

The door opened before she had a chance to answer and Dr. Tyson came in. "Well, good morning, Roxanne," he said brightly, "getting ready for your discharge next week?" The whole floor was eager to give her a big sendoff.

"Fuck you," she said. "You know, Dr. Tyson, if you had

anything but Kotex between your ears, you'd know I need a psychiatrist!"

He glanced at Karen with admiration. "You mean that? That's great!" He seemed genuinely enthusiastic.

Tears were forming in Roxanne's eyes, and to cover up she talked a blue streak. "You think you're getting rid of me, Tyson, but you're not. I still expect you to come to visit me in the rubber room. I mean, there's no getting rid of Roxanne! Into every life a little Roxanne must fall. It makes the fucking flowers bloom."

It was Joan's day off, but Karen figured she would give her a call at home.

"Hi, Joanie," she said cheerfully. "Guess what? I'm finished with Roxanne."

"Terrific," Joan mumbled.

"I feel like celebrating. How about dinner and a movie? My treat."

Karen could hear Joan fumbling with the receiver. "Uh, sorry, Kar'. Got a date." Her voice was slurred. "I mean I'd love to, but Mackey's coming."

"Well, okay," said Karen, "we'll make it some other time."

"Yeah, sure. You caught me indisposed . . ." Her voice trailed off. "Catch you later. Oh no, I got a date. Mackey. Give me a call sometime."

Karen hung up the phone. September suddenly felt cold. She remained on the street corner for a few moments, remembering Sarah's words. It was four-thirty in the afternoon. And Joan was obviously drunk.

# *SIX*

## *October*

Lydia Reese stood in front of the long mirror in the Astor Fifteen locker room. It was a beautiful fall day, but Lydia wasn't looking at the view. She was studying her body and in particular a blotchy red rash that followed a straggling path down her chest, as if somebody had spilled a glass of cranberry juice on her.

She looked with a kind of detached horror—panic mingled with a nurse's clinical curiosity. A cold sweat appeared on her forehead. She moved closer to the mirror and examined the slightly raised surface of the rash.

Two other staff nurses came, laughing, into the locker room. Reflectively, Lydia picked up her blouse and held it to her chest. The two nurses turned into her aisle.

"Do you believe this?" the older one said, reading an interdepartmental memo. "Do you believe they're putting off a decision on the nurses' notes for another couple of months?"

"I could believe anything about the board," the other one replied.

"How about you, Lydia? What do you think about the latest from Monster Morgan?"

When Lydia didn't answer the older woman turned toward her. "Oh, my God. Look at you!" On Lydia's back was another large splotch of red. "You're all broken out!"

Lydia nodded and let her blouse fall onto the bench. "We'd better get you down to Health Service," the older nurse said.

Suddenly the younger nurse screamed. In the joints of her own elbows were two nearly identical red patches.

The Astor Fifteen epidemic had begun.

"Dr. Rizzo," Clare said calmly, "I understand the severity of the problem."

"Do you?" he asked. Although Charles Rizzo was a world-famous neurosurgeon, he was the antithesis of what one might have expected. With his tight T-shirt and blue jeans, he looked more like a construction worker than a doctor. He paced in front of Clare's desk, chain-smoking. "Then get a nurse for Patrick. He can't be left on floor care with this shortage."

"I've tried. But it's hard to get a nurse to work in a unit where there's a hemolytic strep," said Clare.

"Why don't we just shut down the whole hospital and be done with it?" said Dr. Rizzo. "What about private nurses?"

"Whose department is going to pay for that?" she asked.

"Not mine. We'll put it on the floating emergency fund," he said.

"You clear it with Dr. Stover, and I'll get a nurse for Patrick."

It had been several weeks since Karen got off Roxanne's case. She had been working on a cardiac case that had finished two days before. She had decided to take a break and finally began redecorating her apartment. She was up on a ladder, trying to wrestle a wet piece of wallpaper into submission, when the phone rang. Freeing herself from the paper's embrace, she managed to catch the phone just before Clare hung up.

"Good, you're home," Clare said. "Got a minute?"

"Do you know anything about spackling, Clare?"

"Listen, Karen," Clare interrupted. "This isn't just a social call. I've got a big favor to ask."

"Let's hear it," said Karen, interested.

"We need a nurse tomorrow morning at eight for a quadriplegic on Astor Fifteen. Interested?" asked Clare.

"Okay. Who's hiring me—you or the family?"

"I am, or rather Riverview. We've got a kind of contact dermatitis going around. We gave a few of the nurses sick leave for a week. Nothing serious, but it left us short of nurses."

"Contact dermatitis?" Karen repeated.

"I don't think there's any danger. After all, I'm here, and I have a family."

"You're the captain of the ship," said Karen. "You've probably hidden your rash with makeup and checked into a hotel room to protect your kids."

"I'd be the first one out of here if there was any danger," said Clare. But she found Karen's opinion of her flattering.

On Astor Fifteen, however, Karen found pandemonium. The few nurses who were left were grumbling; they scurried around trying to handle an increased case load. Several of the aides, who had not had rashes, had taken off anyway. This made the neuro service even more shorthanded than Clare had implied.

Karen turned when she heard her name being called.

"Hello, I'm Jennifer Warren. You must be Karen Bovit. Welcome to the neuro unit—or what's left of it."

Karen laughed. They shook hands.

"Getting down to business, why don't you tell me about my case?" said Karen.

"Well, the first thing to know is that Patrick Strahan is a really nice guy. The next thing to know is that he has been in this hospital for almost a year."

"How's that possible?"

"Insurance problems. He's a cervical-five cord injury. Patrick fell off a scaffold last year. Now the insurance company's investigating his claim."

"Is the damage permanent?" Karen asked.

"Paralyzed from the neck down," said Jennifer, nodding. "You'll like him. He's got a great personality and he's coping well with the situation. It's his wife who's having the problem coping," Jennifer said.

"In what way?"

"She's pretty bitter. They're in the prime of life—early forties. She's miserable. This is what her marriage has become—a talking head. She hasn't handled it all that gracefully, if you ask me."

"I can understand that," said Karen.

Jennifer smiled. "Well, I guess you're right. I just wish she wouldn't take it out on the staff."

"What kind of 'insurance problems' does he have?"

"I think they are stalling because they hate to pay the cost of nursing home care," said Jennifer. "You see, Dr. Rizzo did surgery, with no results. An investigation was started to see if the insurance company could wriggle out of paying. Naturally, they couldn't. So now we're just waiting for a nursing home bed."

"I hate insurance companies," said Karen.

"It's a much better case than it sounds," said Jennifer.

"You're going to love Pat. He's an angel, the favorite of the whole floor."

"Good morning, Mr. Strahan, my name is Karen Bovit, and I'm going to be your nurse today." She had to restrain an impulse to try to shake hands.

What Jennifer had failed to tell her about Patrick Strahan was also the most obvious thing—he was a giant. He weighed over three hundred pounds and was six foot four in height. He lay on top of a clean sheet in brand-new red flannel pajamas, which were incongruously childish-looking on such a big man. He was fair-skinned, with reddish-brown hair, white at the temples, and lots of freckles. He had once carried his weight well, but now his muscles were sadly atrophying.

"Why so formal, Karen?" he asked. "Just call me Pat. You'll be amazed to hear this, but I knew you were coming in and I'm anxious to get to know you." Despite his disability, Pat had a friendly, warm expression.

"You knew I was coming?" she asked. "How did you know that?"

"Word travels fast around here," he said. "'The great Karen Bovit is coming,' they told me."

"Pat," she said softly, "your flattery embarrasses me. It's my pleasure to meet you. But I have to agree with your good taste in nurses."

Pat roared. His full, infectious laugh was one thing that hadn't been destroyed in his two-story fall. "Oh, I can see we're gonna get along."

"Shall we get down to it?" she asked. "Do you want to tell me about your routine?"

"I do, I do," said Pat, "I'll tell you everything. But first there's a little ritual you must submit to." He lifted his eyebrows at her surprised expression and laughed.

"What's that?" she asked with equal playfulness.

"I always order two cups of coffee so the nurse who is lucky enough to get me can have some breakfast to fortify herself for the ordeal." He nodded in the direction of two Styrofoam cups on the tray.

"Well, thank you. Thank you very much!" Karen said with genuine delight. "Oi think oi'll jest wosh me 'ands and 'ang up the old coat," she said in her best Eliza Doolittle accent. When Karen was nervous she sometimes went overboard to amuse people.

"Hey, that's not bad!" Patrick said enthusiastically. "Karen Bovit, star of stage and screen. I can see it now. Can you do an Irish accent? That might go down a bit smoother with us Strahans."

Karen smiled, and alternately drank her own coffee and spoon-fed Patrick his. It seemed so incredible that this huge and once powerful man now had to be spoon-fed like a baby. It twisted her heart.

"This coffee's not bad, is it?" he said as she wiped his mouth and dribbling chin. They both knew it tasted terrible.

At ten o'clock Karen was returning to Pat with his morning medications. In the hall she ran into a nurse she knew slightly.

"Millie?" she asked.

"Oh, hi, Karen," said the other nurse; she was pleased that Karen remembered her name. Millie was an older nurse, with a sallow complexion. "How are you getting along with Pat? He's usually my assignment," she said, "but because of the shortage of nurses I've had to take more difficult patients."

"I was nervous at first, but I really like him."

"We all love him. He's the nicest man I know. I am so jealous of you, Karen, with just Pat to take care of all day."

She really sounded jealous, too. At least the woman was honest, Karen thought.

"Do you mind if I walk back with you and say hi to Pat?"

"No problem. I'm sure he misses the staff nurses."

When Millie entered the room and saw Pat her face lit up.

"Well, there's my love," Pat said. "Come on over and give me a kiss on the cheek." Millie obeyed, and gave him hers to kiss as well. They gossiped happily. "So the girls still have a rash," said Pat.

"The bubonic plague is more like it," said Millie, laughing.

"No, but what is it really? They say it's some kind of skin rash—I can't pronounce it, but it sounds awful."

"It's nothing serious, really. I'm going to be taking care of you again soon," said Millie, leaving.

It was funny. Karen had to fight down her own feelings of jealousy, although she had known Pat only a few hours. Millie had known him almost a year.

During the following week Karen was still taking care of Patrick. The epidemic was tapering off, but some of the staff nurses were still out. Patrick fascinated Karen. Here was role reversal in its extreme. Pat had been in Riverview so long that the hospital was now his home. The nurses came in to visit him and he took care of them. He was a gracious host and friend. Yet something about it bothered Karen. No one could be more charming than this lovable man. Where did all this charm come from? Karen knew that underneath he was terrified of his total isolation. His dependence was so total.

"Karen, how about another cup of coffee? You look like you could use it," Patrick said.

"Yeah, I'll get us both some coffee," she said. "Okay?" She returned and made herself comfortable to get ready for a long talk. "I'm worried about you, Pat," she said.

"Why?" he asked nervously, lying there like a beached whale. Karen did not know if she would have the heart to continue.

"Do the nurses answer your bell after I leave in the evening? I'm really worried because they're still so under-staffed." Karen could tell by his expression that the topic was making him uncomfortable.

"I try not to bother anybody. They come if I call," he reassured her.

"You're no bother, Pat," said Karen.

"I feel terrible about what I did to Colleen."

"What happened?" asked Karen, hoping to draw him out.

"Well, I mentioned to Millie that she didn't come when I rang." He nodded toward the bell that lay within reach of his head. "Colleen got bawled out."

"She should have gotten worse than a bawling out. She shouldn't keep you waiting at all."

"It's nothing you should worry about, Karen. I don't want you worrying," he said easily. "Old Patrick knows how to take care of himself."

Doris Strahan sat in Clare's office. She was a small, prim woman with dyed black hair that only accentuated her ravaged face. "I understand all this about your nursing shortage," Doris said impatiently. "But this new nurse is spoiling Pat."

Clare sighed. "Do you have any specific complaints?"

"As a matter of fact, I do. She doesn't leave until seven o'clock. She buys him juice from the health food store. She gave him her radio." The outburst stopped as suddenly as it started.

"It happens that Karen Bovit and I went to school together. Everything you've said could be taken two ways. I could make an argument that it's an example of extremely dedicated nursing care.''

Pat's wife suddenly looked defeated. "Miss Henson. My husband is going into a nursing home soon. Spoiling him rotten is just going to make it harder for him to adjust.'' She picked up her bag from the floor. "Thank you for your time anyway,'' she said, and left.

Clare reflected. It didn't take her long to realize her affection for Karen had stood in the way of her judgment. The woman was right. Clare made up her mind to talk to her friend.

One afternoon Karen was reading to Pat from a sports magazine when the door opened and in walked Doris Strahan.

"Would you like me to leave?" Karen asked politely.

"No, stay,'' Pat said quickly. Karen sensed that he needed her at that moment.

Mrs. Strahan ignored her and walked over to Pat and kissed him. "The kids miss you,'' she whispered. "Sheila said she'd be here, but she had a date.''

"With who?'' asked Pat, sincerely interested.

Karen interrupted. "I'm going to take lunch now.''

Doris looked at her watch. "Lunch?'' It was after 2 P.M.

Pat said, "Good idea, Karen. It's not good for you to skip lunch every day.''

"I'll be back in an hour,'' Karen said. She left.

The Riverview cafeteria was almost deserted at this hour. Karen picked out German chocolate cake and a large milk and sat at a window table.

"Hey, you'd better watch it,'' said a familiar voice, "or they'll have to cart you out of here in a wheelbarrow.''

She turned. It was Joan. Karen was glad to see her. They

exchanged kisses and Karen thought she smelled the faint odor of liquor on her friend's breath.

"Let me join you for a couple of minutes," said Joan.

"I'm really glad I bumped into you," Karen said, upset. "I just had the worst problem upstairs with my patient's wife."

"I detest families," Joan said easily.

"I pride myself on getting along with everyone, but this woman is impossible. I honestly believe she's jealous of me."

"What did she say?" asked Joan.

"It's more the way she looks than anything she says," Karen replied heatedly. "She tries to ignore me."

"What's the big deal?" said Joan. "I wish they'd ignore me."

Karen felt frustrated. Joan didn't seem to understand or care.

Ellen Garrison approached the two friends. "Hi," she said.

Karen jumped up. "Ellen, it's great to see you. Why don't you join us? I wanted to tell you your little girl is the sweetest thing—" She stopped short.

Ellen realized immediately that Karen might not want Joan to know she had been at a meeting of the rank and file, and said nothing.

"What are you doing here?" Joan asked.

"I came to appeal for reinstatement," she said.

"I sure hope you get it, Ellen," Karen said.

"Lots of luck," Joan said sarcastically.

"Have you seen the latest leaflet?" Ellen asked, lowering her voice. She handed them each a copy. Joan handed hers back without even looking at it. Karen, embarrassed by Joan, read it aloud:

## "RIVERVIEW NURSES!

"At our last meeting, we unanimously decided that
Riverview nurses had to take action for the safety of the
patients.

"The board had said that it would vote on the proposal
to integrate nurses' and doctors' notes. Now they have
announced another unpardonable delay, this one caused
by Dr. Stover's trip abroad.

"Clare Henson's proposal must prevail! No more
delays! We must not allow Monster Morgan and her
lackey Mackey to threaten the patients' lives and keep
our profession in the Dark Ages.

"Lend your support. Come to our next meeting.

"——RANK-AND-FILE NURSES"

Karen finished a bit nervously. "I just wish they'd stop
making personal attacks."

Ellen blushed. "It's true, though," she said defensively.

"Lackey Mackey! It's not Phil Mackey's fault that you
lost your job, Ellen." Joan looked disgusted.

"I never said it was," said Ellen. She smiled at Karen
and left.

"That was very insensitive of you," said Karen. "That
woman is raising a child alone."

"She should have thought about that before she got
involved with the rank-and-file group," said Joan compla-
cently. "You can spend your whole life worrying about
other people, Karen."

"What's that supposed to mean?" Karen was about to be
baited into a silly argument when she realized that Joan was
not entirely sober.

When she returned, Patrick was lying there with tears in
his eyes. Doris Strahan was standing in the corner, looking
out the window, a twisted Kleenex in her hand.

"What's wrong, Pat?" Karen asked quietly.

Pat started to answer, but Doris made a face. "Let's not wash dirty linen in public," she said urgently.

"I'd like to hear what she thinks of this." Pat's cheerfulness was threadbare.

"She'll take your side, of course. Nobody thinks about what I'm going through."

"What are you going through?" asked Karen sympathetically.

Doris took a deep breath and turned to face them. "Well, I told Pat that I'm not going to be coming here three and four times a week from now on." She paused. "It's too much. Look, I have a full-time job, plus keeping up the house."

"It must be very difficult for you," said Karen, thinking to herself that Pat had it worse than she did.

"I'm exhausted!" said Doris. "It's a long walk from the train to the hospital." Karen nodded. "What do you know about it? You probably take taxis to work."

"I understand, honey," said Pat. "I really do." He had stopped crying.

"Well, Mrs. Strahan," Karen said, "I'm sure Pat will be well taken care of whether you come here or not." Karen hadn't meant to sound snide. It was the wrong thing to say.

"Is that so?" Doris asked bitterly. "Well, we'll see about that. Because one of these days you'll be gone, Millie'll be gone, and then there won't be anyone to take care of him but me. Nobody but me. The *real* wife."

Karen winced at the vehemence of her attack. She was about to respond, when Pat said, "Don't take it out on Karen, honey. She only means well. Of course, nobody knows how hard you've got it. How could they?" His words were sweet, but Karen noticed how frightened his eyes looked.

* * *

On the following morning Clare was waiting for Karen at the nurses' station on the neuro floor. She broke off her conversation with Jennifer when Karen stepped off the elevator.

"Hi, how are you doing?" Clare asked, coming over to her. "Can I talk to you for a minute?"

"Sure," said Karen. "What's up?"

"Can we go in here?" She led Karen into an empty room and sat down. "Could you tell me what is happening here?" Clare asked seriously.

"How do you mean?"

"Well, I've had several visits from the wife of your patient, Mrs. Doris Strahan. Do you want to tell me what's going on between you two?"

The color left Karen's face. She tried to collect her thoughts. "You know, this is incredible," she said finally. "What did she say about me?" Her hand was shaking.

"Calm down," said Clare. "I'll tell you what she said. She claims you're creating a personal problem between herself and her husband. She believes your relationship with Pat will make his adjustment to a nursing home all the more difficult."

"I don't believe this!" Karen said, jumping up. "She said that?" She was so angry she could hardly speak. "I don't know why she said that. Do you want to hear what's really going on?"

"I definitely want to hear what you have to say," Clare said reassuringly. She could see that Karen was far from objective concerning Pat.

"The situation is simply this, Clare. The woman doesn't want to visit her husband anymore. She is going through her angry-at-the-world phase. He's of no use to her—just a liability in her eyes. She hates all the nurses."

Clare smiled weakly. "Karen, I don't know where to begin. I'm not in the room with you, and so it's impossible for me to pass judgment. I did sense some resentment on her part toward the nursing staff. But we also need to talk about your feelings for a minute."

"What do you mean, my feelings?" Karen asked. She was frustrated and confused by Clare's calm demeanor.

"Karen, I don't want to sound like a broken record. Do you remember your patient Eric Sadler?"

"This is a completely different situation," Karen said desperately.

"No, it's not. You have a problem separating your personal emotions from your professional responsibilities."

"Is that a crime?"

"No, it's not a crime," said Clare gently. "I understand that you've been spending your own money for gifts and food."

"Gifts! I gave him an old radio I never use!" She laughed indignantly. "Yes, I bought him some magazines and books."

Clare sensed she was missing the point of the conversation. She tried again. "Kar', nobody's questioning your dedication. You're an excellent nurse. I'm just concerned about a life that's overinvolved with patients."

That stopped Karen short. Clare pressed her advantage. "And what about this?" Clare detached some papers from her clipboard and handed them to Karen.

"What about it?"

"Well, who else would go to the library, research all these articles on quadriplegics, and then make copies to give the other nurses?"

"So?"

"So you don't see anything strange in that?"

"No, not at all," said Karen defensively. "What I find

strange is that you would bring this up. I practice nursing the way I believe it should be practiced," said Karen.

"Joan was right. You've got a blind spot on this topic," Clare said, sighing. "I mean, dedication is one thing, but this is getting ridiculous. Why don't you try being less of the perfect nurse for a while? You might be a happier person."

"Joan said that?" Karen laughed bitterly.

"She just mentioned—"

"Listen, Clare, was she drunk or sober when she 'mentioned' this?"

Clare was caught up short. After a pause she asked, "What do you mean by that?"

"I mean," said Karen defiantly, "that Joan is not in a position to comment on my personal problems."

Clare was taken by surprise and momentarily deflated by this. She hugged her clipboard. It wasn't the first time Joan's drinking had been mentioned to her.

"If that's true," she said slowly, "I'll look into it and deal with it. But don't confuse the issue. You've gotten yourself too deeply involved in this case. I'm beginning to doubt my own judgment in hiring you."

"Oh. That's not the tune you were singing the other week when you begged me to come in," Karen said bitterly. She stood up to leave. "I like working here, Clare, but I can work elsewhere, too, you know."

"Kar', I'm sorry," Clare said suddenly. "We're both upset."

Karen stopped. Softening also, she said, "You're right. For the life of me, though, I don't know what you're trying to prove, Clare. If it's such a small thing, why don't we both just drop it?"

Clare pursed her lips but decided the best course was to say nothing.

\* \* \*

By the end of the month, however, the problem solved itself. Clare invited Karen to attend Nursing Grand Rounds, a monthly hospital seminar, with her. The topic was "Nursing Burnout."

"I guess you think they really zeroed in on my problem," Karen said afterward, trying to make a joke.

"One of your many," Clare said, joking back. "Seriously, I thought it was a good seminar, didn't you? I wish Joan could have made it in."

"Well, I have to hurry back to Pat now. This was a long lunch hour."

Clare seemed embarrassed. "I wanted to talk to you about Patrick." Karen braced herself for another lecture. "His insurance came through. He's being transferred to a nursing home in the suburbs."

The color drained from Karen's face. "Well, I'll need time to prepare him for it," she said. "He's dreadfully afraid of leaving here. I've been working with him for the past week trying to get him ready—"

"Karen, there's no easy way to end this."

Suddenly Karen felt a knot form in the pit of her stomach. She knew what was going on. "They're taking him now, aren't they, Clare?"

"Yes."

She rushed upstairs to find him. She couldn't believe this was happening. How do you take a man like Pat and warehouse him in a nursing home? When she got to his room he was gone. Karen was stunned.

"Can I help you, Karen?"

It was Millie.

"I came to see Pat," she said, panting.

"Pat," said Millie sadly. "Pat's gone."

"When?"

"His wife and daughter just came to take him away in an ambulance." She sighed. "I'm gonna miss the big guy. The floor just won't be the same without him."

Karen rushed back downstairs. There was a clear view through the lobby, right out to the curbside, but there was no ambulance there. She ran around to the side entrance where the ambulances sometimes pulled up. There was Pat, surrounded by four orderlies, his wife and daughter standing by.

"Pat!" Karen called, out of breath from running. The women turned, and Pat tried to lean his head backward, to look at her upside down. She came around to him.

"Oh, hiya, Karen," he said. "Honey, you remember Karen, don't you?" His voice seemed subdued and somehow distant.

"Pat, they didn't tell me," Karen said. "I knew nothing about it—" The words could hardly come out; she choked on each of them. Karen felt that she was making a fool of herself, but she didn't care.

"Oh, don't worry about it. It's an awfully nice nursing home, isn't it, sweetheart?" he asked his wife.

Doris Strahan smiled. "We appreciate your concern, Miss Bovit," Doris said. "Pat isn't going to need any private nurses. He's got us now."

Tears welled up in Karen's eyes. The ambulance drivers were growing visibly restless, eager to beat the late afternoon traffic on the highway. Karen placed her hand on Pat's face and held it there for a moment.

"I'll come visit you," she said finally.

"Sure, that'd be swell," said Pat, but Karen knew he was frightened. "That would be okay, wouldn't it, dear?"

Doris Strahan nodded.

Without further ado, the hospital orderlies collapsed Pat's gurney and helped the ambulance attendants lift the burden into the ambulance. The ambulance edged away from the curb, then picked up speed, lights flashing. Karen watched it for as long as she could.

"Whew! Dead weight!" said one of the orderlies, wiping his hands on the legs of his greens. Karen rubbed her eyes with the back of her hand and then slowly walked back into the hospital.

# SEVEN

## November

Clare and her husband sat in the breakfast nook of their house, drawing up the guest list for Ken's thirty-fifth birthday party. They sat next to each other on an overstuffed sofa, a big quilt pulled up over them to fend off the November chill. Clare wrote neatly, using the Sunday newspaper as her lap desk.

After they had agreed on ten or fifteen names, Ken asked, "How about your friends Karen and Joan?"

Clare smiled. "I'm not sure I want to invite them."

"How come?" Ken asked, genuinely surprised.

"I don't know . . ." She trailed off. "Joan's becoming a bit of a problem for me now. And if I don't invite Joan, and invite Karen, that will really cause trouble."

Ken pulled back his arm. "Oh, come on! This is a social event. It's not a business meeting. And it's my birthday," he said petulantly.

"You know, Ben Kendall's coming, and lots of other people from the hospital." Clare's voice was tinged with defensiveness. "The truth is, I'm afraid Joan'll get drunk and do something embarrassing."

"If she does something embarrassing," said Ken, "that's her problem. I haven't seen either of them since college. And I've asked you a dozen times to invite them up."

"Okay," said Clare with resignation. "I'll invite them both, but I hope Joan can keep her hands to herself. And Karen'll probably be too busy poring over case records to come to a mere party." They both laughed.

"It should be interesting," Ken said. He took the magazine section from her. "And now, if you don't mind, I'm going to start the puzzle. Let me see," he said, smiling. "What's a four-letter word for a chronic alcoholic? Starts with a J."

Clare thought for a minute, then punched him in the arm. Laughing, she added Karen's and Joan's names to the list in big bold letters.


"What do you mean, you don't want to go?" Karen said.

It was Saturday morning, and she was sitting in Joan's apartment on the north side of the city. It was basically one room, with a kitchen alcove, a bathroom, and two walk-in closets. In one of the closets Joan had set up a tiny office, piled high with papers and books. The main room itself was practically taken up with an unmade sofa bed, a wall unit she had saved from her marriage, and the folding chair Karen sat on.

"Let's discuss this," said Joan groggily. "Can I get you some coffee?"

"I'll get it," said Karen. She went into the small kitchenette and was about to take a cup when she spied a bug crawling between the sink and the stove. "On second thought," she said, "let's just grab something on the road. C'mon, already, it's past nine."

"Damn, I feel just awful," said Joan. She looked at herself in the bathroom mirror, pulling down her bottom eyelid to reveal a frightening complex of red veins. Karen saw her take a vigorous swig from a bottle of Maalox.

"Stomach trouble? You'd better mend your wicked ways, Joan, or you're going to get an ulcer."

"Mind your own business," Joan muttered. "I'm taking a shower. My hair smells like tobacco."

Karen picked up a copy of *Ms.* and started skimming from the back. She was eager to get on their way and was annoyed with Joan. She had gone to the trouble of renting a car and she wanted to hit the road.

A strange cry came from the bathroom.

"What?"

"Mmmrrr . . . brrrr . . . mrrrr . . ." Joan stuck her head out from behind the shower curtain. She had a mouthful of toothpaste froth. "D'ya think we have to get him a present?"

"I bought him a book," Karen said.

"A book!" said Joan, spitting a mouthful of toothpaste in a stream. "Do you think he knows how to read?"

"It's that best-seller on the construction industry. I thought he would enjoy it."

Joan laughed. "Do you remember Ken well? For me he's kind of a blur. Construction. A boring job for a boring guy."

"You don't like Ken?" Karen shouted above the sound of the shower.

"He's okay," said Joan, letting the water play on her breasts. "He came on to me once, you know."

"Oh, give me a break," said Karen.

"He was cute in his way. I'm curious to see what he looks like now."

"Then you're coming?" Karen asked.

"Okay, okay," said Joan, turning off the water and grabbing a dirty-looking towel.

"You're too much," Karen said. "Hurry up. I don't think we should keep the birthday boy waiting."

On the trip out of the city in Karen's rented car Joan slept. She looked a lot healthier when she awoke, just as they entered Clare's neighborhood.

"My mouth feels like the bottom of a bird cage. Hey, this place is like Dick-Jane-and-Spot. How cute!"

"I bet it's nice to raise kids here," said Karen. She sounded a bit envious.

"I'm going to explode if I don't get to a bathroom soon," said Joan. "Riding in a car does that to me. It drives Mackey crazy."

"Good. 'Cause it drives me crazy too."

"I wish I hadn't fallen asleep, it gives me morning breath." She brushed her teeth with her finger.

"Look, Joan," Karen said impatiently, "what I need for you to do now is read directions." She pulled out the printed instructions, which had been stuck in the ashtray.

"Do you think my present is adequate, Kar'?"

"Under the circumstances, it'll have to do." Karen smiled. There had been simply no place to stop on the way up, so at the last minute they frantically raided a Howard Johnson's and bought their most expensive box of saltwater taffy.

"Sure hope he's not diabetic," said Joan, laughing.

"I think this is it!" Karen said excitedly. "See all the cars?"

"Is my makeup on straight?" asked Joan, suddenly nervous. "Do you really think the present is okay?"

"I'll tell you what—we'll say that both presents are from the two of us."

"That's a great idea. You're not half bad as a friend, you

know?" said Joan. She spontaneously reached over and kissed Karen on the cheek. "Keep your eye on me today, okay?" she asked tentatively. "I'm not going to drink. Just, you know, keep me on the track."

Karen smiled at her reassuringly.

The Henson house stood on the corner—a white center-hall colonial with freshly painted blue shutters. In the back was a barn-turned-garage. It housed the family's small station wagon and an old Mustang Ken was working on. The beautifully colored maple trees had begun to shed their leaves.

"I'm really glad you could make it," said Clare, taking their hands. "Come on inside. It's too cold to stand around talking. Now I'll have someone to gossip with," she giggled in a whisper. Clare looked relaxed and almost elegant, in a white silk smock and black pants.

"You remember Ken," she said, leading them to him.

"How could we ever forget?" said Joan, reaching up and kissing him gently.

"Watch that!" Clare said playfully.

Karen and Ken shook hands—then made a few comical feints toward each other, unsure whether to kiss or not. They were like two strangers bumping into each other on the street. In the end they did kiss, everyone laughing a bit too loudly. She handed him the book and he thanked her while opening it. "Oh, that's great, I've been wanting to read this."

In her mind, everything was as Karen had imagined it. There were tasteful oil paintings hanging on every wall. Clusters of well-dressed people, some of whom she recognized from the hospital, stood around laughing and talking. There were children wandering in and out but spending most of their time in the basement family room. On the periphery of a Riverview group stood Ben Kendall.

Clare's son approached his parents. "Hey, Dad, can I have the keys to the car?" He wasn't even a teenager.

"Going for a drive?" Ken asked, lifting his glasses.

"Sure, Dad. I just want to show Jennifer the new CD player."

"Kenny, I'd like you to meet Karen and Joan," said Clare. "They're my oldest friends."

"That sounds terrible," said Joan.

"Is this your son?" Karen asked.

At Clare's prodding, Kenny shook hands and mumbled hello.

"He seems very nice," said Karen. "He's awfully big, though. How old is he?"

"Nine," said Clare. "He's such a rascal. What do you think of him?"

"He looks so much like you!" Karen said. "I can't believe you've got such grown-up kids."

"Some rug rat," said Clare, glancing at Joan. "Can I get you something to drink?"

"Sure," said Karen. "What do you have?"

"Everything," said Ken. He pointed to a well-equipped bar.

"What are you drinking, Ken?" Karen asked.

"Ken doesn't drink," said Clare proudly. "He's in training for a marathon."

"I'm impressed," she said. "When does that happen?"

"In the spring," said Ken. "Running is such a natural high."

Karen glanced over at Joan and they exchanged looks. They would have something to laugh about in the car going home.

"Well, I'll have a glass of white wine," said Karen.

"And how about you, Joan? Same thing?" Ken asked, a touch of irony in his voice.

"What? Drink. Oh no, thank you. Maybe a glass of orange juice, that's all."

"Okay. Are you sure?" he asked. Joan nodded nonchalantly.

"Mommy, Kenny won't let me put on *my* records!" It was Becky, Clare's daughter. She was a pale, wispy blonde who sneaked glances at Karen and Joan with shy doe eyes.

"Kids, please don't fight," Clare said, trying to remain calm. "Take turns."

"That's what I told him," said Becky. "And tell his friends to stop teasing me," she said, unable to take her eyes off the visitors.

"Do you think this will do?" Ken asked Karen. He had returned with a bottle of expensive California wine.

"Sure, anything," said Karen. "I mean, yes, that's wonderful," she added when she saw his disappointment. "So, Ken, tell me about the construction business."

"Not much to tell. By the way, thanks again for the book. You know, they say part of it is based on my company."

"Is that right?" asked Clare.

"Yeah, the part about the layoffs," said Ken. Karen laughed nervously. "No, I'm serious. We even made *The Wall Street Journal*. Luckily, I'm hanging on, because of seniority, but a lot of the fellas are hurting very badly. Anyway, I'll enjoy the book." He poured a glass of wine and handed it to Karen ceremoniously. "And what about you, Karen? How have you been? You look terrific. You always did dress for the occasion."

"I always undress for the occasion," said Joan, giggling uncomfortably.

"Mommy, Mommy!" Becky cried. "Stephanie's here." She ran into the hall.

Clare turned to her friends and explained. "Stephanie's our next-door neighbor's daughter," Clare confided. "Becky worships her. She's been very sick, though, and Becky hasn't seen her recently."

Nancy Taylor held out her hand. "Hi, Clare. I'm awfully sorry to drag Stephie around, but we just couldn't get a baby-sitter. She was desperate to get out of the house, and she is feeling a little better."

"Hi, Stephanie," said Karen. "How old are you?"

"Twelve," said Stephanie reluctantly. She was a pretty girl, with ivory skin and dark eyes, made darker by the rings around them. Becky drew her aside and they talked.

"Is she really twelve?" Joan asked Clare quietly.

"She's small for her age," said Clare.

Joan was shocked and surprised at the appearance of Stephanie. What's wrong with this child? she wondered.

"Joan," said Ken, brandishing the bottle, "are you sure you—oh, hi, Nancy. I didn't see you come in. And Stephanie, are you feeling a little better?"

Stephanie smiled wanly. "Can I watch TV upstairs?" she asked.

"Sure," Clare said. "You lie down in the guest room."

Becky said, taking her hand, "She can come to my room. I'll take care of her."

Clare was about to follow, when Joan said, "You and Nancy can stay with the party, Clare. I'll make sure that they settle in."

"Are you sure?" Clare asked searchingly.

"Yes, boss," said Joan. "Quite sure. I'll be down in a few minutes."

The two little girls seemed to take to Joan immediately and were thrilled to have her company. Karen was surprised to see how easily the three were chit-chatting as they went up the stairs.

"Stephanie's looking somewhat better," Clare said unconvincingly. "Come on, Nancy. I want you to meet some of my friends from work. There's Dr. Kendall. Karen, do you know him? If not, I'll introduce you."

Upstairs, Stephanie got into the spare bed in Becky's room. Joan slouched in a yellow beanbag chair and addressed the girls. "How long have you two been friends?" she asked, continuing their easy conversation.

"Well, really close friends for about two months," said Becky. "Because Stephie can't go to school. So I bring her assignments and books and things."

"A two-month vacation from school?" said Joan, joking. "Sounds like fun."

"I hate it," said Stephanie with emotion. "I have to take pills all the time. It gives me an upset stomach. One time I broke out all over my body. It was horrible!"

"What does the doctor say is wrong with you, Stephanie?"

"They don't know," she said with adultlike resignation.

"What kind of medicine are you taking?" Joan asked with professional interest.

"Antibiotics."

"Do you know the name?" asked Joan.

"Well, they keep changing them every couple of weeks," said Stephanie. "The black and yellow one was so big Becky's mother had to come over and put it in yogurt. Ugh!"

Joan thought this over. The child had obviously been through a lot. "I'm sure you'll be well soon," she said. "I hope this is the worst that ever happens to you."

Becky wanted to join in. "I was in the hospital. When I was three I had my tonsils out. Mommy tells me I was very good. But I don't remember it."

"I've been in the hospital a lot," said Stephanie. "Two years ago I broke my arm in the playground on the rings."

"That could be serious," Joan said sympathetically.

"It was," said Becky. "She had to have an operation, and everything. We went to visit her."

Joan was surprised and interested. "What kind of an operation?"

Becky vied for her attention. "She had to have shots, she had to have blood, she had to have a needle in her arm. She had a big cast, we wrote our names on it. . . ."

Stephanie interrupted with a prolonged wet-sounding cough, which she had difficulty halting. Joan went over and wiped her face with a tissue, taking the opportunity to feel her neck. She ran through the obvious possibilities: whooping cough, strep throat, pneumonia. None of them quite fit the picture. The most disturbing fact was that Stephanie had obviously not responded to multiple courses of antibiotics. She wondered about the quality of medical care in this sleepy suburb.

"I didn't mind the cast," said Stephanie after she finished coughing, "till it started to itch. But I hated the diarrhea the most."

"Did you bleed a lot?" Joan asked. Something was disturbing her.

"I guess so," Stephanie said weakly.

"You mean they gave you a transfusion?" asked Joan.

"A few of them, I think," said Stephanie. "Can we watch TV now?"

"My mom says everybody should give blood to the blood bank," said Becky proudly.

Joan felt a surge of panic. No, it couldn't be, she thought. Impossible.

Just then Clare poked her head in the door. "Came to check up on you," she said. "Everything okay?"

Joan didn't answer at first. "The kids are just about to watch TV," she said finally. She added, with a strange intensity, "Clare, when you get a chance, I have to talk to you."

Karen had been looking forward to the party all week. It was a most pleasant surprise to find that Ben Kendall was there as well.

Karen and Ben were both shy and this made small talk virtually impossible for them. After several false starts Karen said, "I think it's great you're involved with the rank-and-file nurses' group. It makes the group seem more well rounded to have other disciplines involved. . . ."

Ben seemed surprised. "I'm sorry, I didn't see you at the meeting," he said. Lowering his voice, he said, "Does Clare know that you're involved with the group?"

"I haven't gotten around to telling her yet," she said, laughing.

"Me neither," he said with a smile. "Do you think she might want to join up?"

"You've got to be kidding," said Karen. "She has a full-time job convincing Charlotte she didn't start the group."

"Monster Morgan," he added in a low voice. He laughed heartily. He had a gap between his two front teeth. It was the kind of imperfection that made him look boyish and, to Karen, more attractive.

"Lackey Mackey," she replied, as if giving a password. They laughed together.

Joan approached. "I hate to break in," she said seriously, "but I need to bounce something off you."

Karen sighed inwardly. "Sure, Joan. Do you know Dr. Kendall?"

"Yes," he said. "We met on the Heather Asher case, do you remember? I'm her oncologist."

"Of course, Doctor," said Joan. "Now let me get to the point. Stephanie Taylor—the little girl who came in before—is a very sick child." Her seriousness arrested their attention. "I don't want to criticize the medical care she's been getting up here, but we all know these are the boonies." She paused. "She has had several courses of antibiotics, none of which has arrested a terrible pneumonia-like cough."

"What do you think it is?" asked Karen curiously.

Joan hesitated and looked at Ben Kendall. "The child had a transfusion for a broken arm two years ago."

"Does she have swollen glands? Diarrhea?"

She nodded. "Both."

Suddenly Karen felt left out. "What are you thinking?" she asked.

Ben and Joan exchanged a glance, and Joan turned to Karen. "I don't know what's wrong, but I've got a terrible feeling."

Ben said, "Karen, the symptoms Joan is describing are not inconsistent with a diagnosis of acquired immune deficiency syndrome."

Karen's eyes widened. "Pediatric AIDS?"

"She had a blood transfusion two years ago," Joan said.

The three were suddenly silent as Ken came up and said, "Freshen anyone's drink?"

It was Joan who first recovered her composure. "Everything's fine, Ken," she said softly. "Could you do me a favor and ask Clare to come here for a minute? It's rather important."

Karen asked Joan to drive home, since she had had a few glasses of wine at the party.

"Do you really think that little girl could have AIDS, Joan?" Karen asked as they pulled away from the house.

"I've worked with a few AIDS cases, but I've never had one who wasn't gay, and I've certainly never seen a kid . . ."

Joan glanced over at her as she drove. "Just because you haven't had a case doesn't mean much, Karen. Actually, it's getting pretty common. You can't rule out AIDS without a test, and that little girl is sick enough to have the test."

Karen thought a bit. "That poor kid. And the poor parents. Do you think Clare will convince them to look for a doctor in the city? It's so awful!" she suddenly exclaimed. It was hard for Karen to separate her personal feelings from her professional curiosity.

"Look, we don't know she has it!" said Joan with annoyance. "I overheard Clare suggesting a few doctors," she said. "They spoke to Ben Kendall, too, and he volunteered to arrange some tests at Riverview." Without looking, she felt for the cigarette lighter on the rented car and lit a cigarette. "It's a bad business," she said, exhaling the smoke out of the side of her mouth.

Karen kept her eyes glued to the road. "Joan, would you mind blowing your smoke out the window, or at least not directly in my face?"

"So," Joan said, deliberately changing the topic, "you seemed to be hitting it off pretty well with Ben Kendall."

Karen smiled guardedly. "He's a pretty nice guy."

"Not my type," said Joan, laughing.

"Too young, Joan?" Karen asked, teasing.

"Too boring. He's one of those research doctors. All he wants to do is sit up nights staring into his microscope." She rolled down the window and tossed the cigarette. "Just your type, I'd think."

"I'm not really interested," said Karen defensively.

"No, of course not," said Joan, laughing to herself. "That's because he's interested in you."

They rode along awhile, looking at the bruised and cloudy sky over the low mountains. The colors of the foliage would have been beautiful, but now it was dark, and everything was the same dull purple.

"It looks like rain," Karen said.

Joan turned on the radio, which only had AM. She flipped through the dial. "All junk," she said disgustedly, and shut it off without waiting for Karen's opinion.

Karen said nothing but kept her eyes on the road. After a while it turned into a busy route of gas stations, furniture outlets, and diners with huge American flags.

"You know, Joan," Karen said suddenly. "I was really proud of you today."

"Yeah, I was sort of proud of myself," Joan said, smiling. "Didn't touch a thing all day. You see, I don't need to drink, really. I just do it to be sociable."

"I didn't mean that," said Karen. "I was talking about your diagnostic skills."

"Oh, that," said Joan. She sounded really self-deprecating. "Big deal. It was obvious the kid had something worse than a cold. Anyone would have picked up on it. Anybody but one of the dummies they have up at those suburban hospitals, that is."

"That's not true," Karen said. "I was there and I didn't notice it. Clare lives next door to her and she didn't notice it. You tease me about being overdedicated, but the fact is, it was you who went up there, palpated her lymph nodes . . ."

"Give me a break," said Joan, laughing. "I was just running away from the party, that's all. It was a place to go. I sympathized with those kids. They were as bored as I was."

"You thought it was a boring party?" Karen asked. "I had a good time."

"Sure, you picked up the only good-looking guy in the place. Could you believe those neighbors of hers? I could never live out in the sticks. Two point six kids, two point six cars, two point six lays per week. What a life! I can't believe what's become of poor old Clare."

"She seems to be happy. It must have its compensations," said Karen.

"You bet it has," Joan snickered. "And when she's nursing director—"

"What?"

"Sure, didn't you know? Charlotte Morgan's probably going to resign next year. She hasn't made up her mind yet. That's the whole reason Clare is so worked up about the nurses' notes. She hopes that if her proposal passes she'll get Charlotte's job."

"I find that hard to believe," said Karen, shocked.

"Don't. Charlotte told Mackey and Mackey told me. Not that I care. I just think it's funny, the way Clare comes off so high and mighty all the time."

They had reached the approach to the bridge, and Joan sped merrily over the corrugated warning pavement. Suddenly, in the distance, there was the wail of a siren. Karen glanced in the passenger side-view mirror and saw red lights.

"Oh no!" Joan cried. "Listen, when they pull me over, you tell them you're too sick to drive."

"What are you talking about?" Karen asked, annoyed. She nervously glanced from Joan to the approaching police car.

"My license . . ." Joan said. "I lost it."

"Lost it?" Karen asked.

"They pulled it last year. Some trumped-up charge."

"Drunken driving?"

"I wasn't drunk," Joan screamed. "I hit a divider, but

legally I wasn't drunk at all. Listen, just say you're pregnant or something. I don't believe this!''

Joan grew panicky as the police car approached. To their surprise, it did not slow as it approached but swerved around them and passed through the tollbooth and onto the bridge.

Karen glanced over at her swiftly. The bridge was well lit, and she could see that one of the strands of Joan's long brown hair had gotten loose and fallen in front of her face. She had been feeling guilty about having mentioned Joan's drinking to Clare. Now she didn't feel guilty at all.

"Joan, have you ever thought maybe you're an alcoholic?" Karen's words were unrehearsed. She hadn't intended to mention Joan's drinking on this trip home, but once she did she was glad she had put it on the table.

To her amazement, Joan did not blow up at her. All she said was, "Come on, just because I lost my license?"

"Not just because of your license. I've noticed lots of things. I've even talked this over with Clare."

Joan took her eyes off the road and glared at Karen. "You little bitch," she said bitterly. "What right do you have to discuss anything about me with Clare?"

"You took an interest in Stephanie, and she was a complete stranger to you. Why shouldn't I take an interest in your health?"

"Well, that's very touching," said Joan. "You saw me at the party today, right? If I had a problem, do you think I could have gone without a drink for so long? I appreciate your concern, but I'm a grown woman. I can take care of myself. That's the difference between Stephanie and me. Stephanie's just a kid. I can take care of myself." Joan studied Karen's face to see if her words were having their desired effect. It was too dark in the car now to tell.

"You know, it's funny," Karen said after a long pause.

"Whenever you try to help someone it seems to be taken wrong."

"Just back off," said Joan. She lit another cigarette and blew the smoke defiantly.

They rode in silence, Karen looking out the window at the row of lighted skyscrapers in the distance. They managed finally to strike up some light conversation on the way downtown. When they got to the North Side, Joan pulled up in front of her apartment and said, "Well, thanks for the ride. Boy, am I tired," she added, yawning. "I'm going right to bed."

"Well, take care of yourself," Karen said, staring right into her eyes.

"Hey, I always do," Joan said, laughing. "And thanks for your help," she added ambiguously, slinging her floppy bag over her shoulder. "Ciao."

Karen got behind the wheel and drove away. She remembered that she had to return the car, and so she circled around the block. The street was dark and empty, except for Joan, walking briskly away from her apartment. Karen couldn't resist the urge to follow slowly behind.

Two blocks later Karen caught sight of the blinking neon sign of the Post Mortem. At that moment Karen knew where Joan was headed. The door opened. There was a blast of loud music and Joan quickly stepped into the bar.

The second week in November, Clare sent for Joan.

"Hi, Clare. By the way, I enjoyed your party. Ken looks better than I remembered him. What ever happened to your neighbor's kid?"

"They've scheduled some tests here," said Clare. She seemed a bit distracted. "I'll let you know as soon as I hear something. Thanks for coming up," she said.

"Did I have any choice?" Joan asked. "I gathered from Sarah that the world was coming to an end. What's up?"

"How was your weekend?" Clare asked evasively.

"Wild—as usual," said Joan, laughing.

"Everything okay with you?" Clare asked, looking straight at her.

"Sure, why?" Joan asked casually.

"Just wondering."

"Can we cut the small talk? What's on your mind, Clare?" Joan asked in a serious tone. "What's the matter?"

"Look, Joan, I don't know exactly how to say this, but I think it's my responsibility as a friend—" Joan exhaled impatiently. "Okay, then," Clare said. "What I want to know, Joan, is, do you think you have a drinking problem?" The silence hung between them.

"Do I have a drinking problem?" Joan repeated. "No, I don't have a drinking problem. Do I drink? Yes, I drink. So what? Is that a crime?"

"No," Clare said slowly. "But you certainly can't drink and do nursing, any more than you can drink and drive."

Joan exploded. "You've obviously been talking to Karen. I don't do either of those things! What do you think I am, stupid?"

"I'm glad to hear you say that," Clare said calmly. She felt in control of the situation now. "Nevertheless, I've had reports that you've been coming to the hospital not quite sober."

Joan was about to yell something about gossipmongers when she remembered that she had been buzzed Friday in the cafeteria. "I don't know what you mean," she said evasively. "I never in my life have dealt with a clinical situation while under the influence of alcohol. Nor, by the way, have I ever driven under the influence. And if Karen told you so, she's full of it."

Clare sat calmly, her hands folded in front of her. She wasn't about to let Joan slip away into the underbrush. "Didn't you show up at Riverview on Friday with alcohol on your breath?"

"How would I know? I can't smell my own breath. Talking of which, Clare, do you remember how at school we tried to gargle the liquor off our breaths when your father showed up unexpectedly?"

It was a funny memory, but Clare wasn't buying. "Look, Joan, you're avoiding the topic. Tell me what you were doing on Friday afternoon?"

"I don't have to," said Joan defiantly. "What is this, *1984?* Big Sister is watching you?"

Clare stared at her, with growing impatience. "All right, Joan. Have it your way."

Joan looked at her in surprise. There was something in Clare's tone that frightened her. "Well, it's no big deal. Listen, I had to meet Dr. Mackey after work. I got here early. I went into the Post Mortem and I spent a couple of hours there waiting. But for God's sake," she said, "I was on my own time. My own time," she repeated. "Do you understand the concept?"

Clare nodded. "And then?"

"What is this?" Joan asked in an anxious voice. "An interrogation?" Clare just stared at her. Joan continued nervously. "Then I came to the cafeteria and I sat down with—" Her face lit up. "Aha, I get it. Karen! I can't believe her!"

"Karen is worried about you. I am too," Clare said calmly.

"'Karen is worried about you,'" Joan mimicked, and her imitation was accurate as usual.

Clare kept a poker face, however. "Go on."

"Well, I ran into Karen in the cafeteria and she poured

out her heart to me about her latest case. Have you ever noticed that Karen's latest case is always the world's most important personal crisis?''

Despite herself, Clare smiled. Having done so, she used the occasion to lighten the mood a little bit. "She does seem to get the most challenging cases," she said with a touch of irony.

Joan was happy to be talking about Karen. "She latches onto her patients because she doesn't have a life outside the hospital."

"Look, Joan. You're avoiding the issue. If you spent two hours in the Post Mortem, you must have been drunk by the time you got out of there."

"Not true," said Joan. "A few drinks, that's all." Clare frowned and nodded, skeptically. "And if you don't believe me," Joan added vehemently, "ask Dr. Mackey. Because I *know* the director of anesthesiology will back me up one hundred proof—I mean, percent," Joan said with a mischievous smile.

# EIGHT

## December

The postman stood on the edge of the apartment house, twelve stories up. A strong winter wind grabbed the end of his regulation blue tie and flapped it up over his shoulder.

"Oh, my God, isn't that the mailman, Mr. Dooley?" yelled a young woman tenant.

"He's going to jump! Someone call the police!"

"No wonder I didn't get any mail," said an older lady.

Mr. Arthur Dooley stepped from the asphalt roof onto the brick ledge and leaned over the edge of the building. If this mailman was despondent, he certainly didn't look like it. In fact he seemed quite elated.

"Security alert!" he yelled. "Phasers stand by! Lay in a course for earth!" He shivered on the brink of the roof. "Assemble the crew!" He gave a boatswain's whistle. "Attention, everyone," he yelled, addressing the growing audience below. "I have communications from Star Fleet Command!" With that, he reached onto his well-worn leather sack and threw several hundred pieces of mail to the *Enterprise* crew" below.

* * *

At Riverview Hospital, Arthur Dooley continued in his role as James T. Kirk, captain of the starship *Enterprise*. "I'm on my way to battle station," he said, trying to rise from the table in the Surgical Intensive Unit. He had been sent to the SICU because every spare bed in the medical ICU was taken by rash victims.

"Please, Mr. Dooley, calm down," Joan Fisher said, exasperated. "We're just trying to take some tests." This didn't make much of an impression, so she added, "You've got a serious liver condition. You don't want to make it worse, do you?"

Mr. Dooley's face was flushed red with excitement, his graying blond hair plastered over his forehead. He suddenly frowned. "Lieutenant Uhura," he addressed Sarah in a stage whisper, "an entire star system's stability depends on our survival. You will instruct Mr. Spock to destroy this planet in one hour if we are not back."

Sarah couldn't help smiling. Joan sighed and continued to try to find a vein in the squirming mailman's arm.

"On second thought, Lieutenant," Art Dooley added with a slightly condescending sneer, "if they want to fight we must get some maneuvering room. Open the hailing frequency, Uhura, identify us, and ask these aliens their intentions."

"Ay, ay, Captain," Sarah said, enjoying the game too much for Joan's taste. "Just humor him," she whispered to Joan.

"Damn," Joan hissed. "I just contaminated another needle. Could you get me some more?" She looked up to heaven for guidance. Her stomach felt queasy. It was past her seven o'clock break but she hadn't eaten yet. Lately she had been eating less and less regularly. With the winter chill, Joan had caught a cold which she couldn't shake. She was feeling worn out and frazzled.

Sarah returned with the needle and four test tubes for the blood samples. "Thanks, Sarah," Joan said. "I don't know how I'm going to get through this night."

"It's not so bad," said Sarah with her usual composure. "Just play along with him. It could have been worse," she said. "He could've thought he was Superman."

"In which case he probably wouldn't be bothering us now, would he?" Joan replied sarcastically.

The two of them held his arm down long enough for Joan to draw the bloods.

"Lieutenant Uhura, did you hear me?" Dooley screamed.

"I always disliked science fiction," said Joan, writing out the label for the last sample. "Now I detest it."

"To him, this is science fact," said Sarah, talking about Dooley as if he weren't there. "Bijan said that when he goes into the manic phase of his manic depression he's really convinced he's Captain Kirk. His sister told the admitting doctor that he's got all the *Star Trek* shows on tape. Why don't they just give him lithium, Joan?" she asked.

"Boy, do I need a vacation," said Joan, washing her hands. "Lithium carbonate? That is his regular medication," she added. "He does very well on it, but recently he developed some kind of liver malfunction. When that flared up, his internist discontinued the lithium."

"So he winds up delivering the U.S. mail from the roof. Did you hear what he told the cops?"

"No, I haven't had a chance to read the admission note yet. What happened?"

"Mr. Dooley decided it would be more efficient for everyone to pick up their mail up off the ground. That way he only had to make one delivery, instead of hundreds. . . ."

"Crew, stand by! Yellow alert!" He turned to Sarah. "Will you tell Her Majesty that Captain Kirk requests the pleasure of a visit?"

"Sarah," said Joan, "you take the blood to the lab. I'll watch Mr. Dooley." After a few minutes Joan went into the break room and sat down, massaging her face with her hands. She felt awful. It was only with an effort that she kept her body from slumping forward onto the table. She reached into her bag, her hands shaking as she took out a Maalox bottle. She took a swig from it. "Christ, am I a wreck," she said to herself, wiping her mouth. "What are you doing here?" she asked, looking up. Sarah was standing in the doorway. "Didn't I tell you to take the bloods to the lab?"

"It's done. I just wondered where you'd gone," Sarah said apologetically. "You don't look too good, Joan."

Joan put down the bottle. "Is that so?" She was about to answer testily but then softened. "Well, you're right. My stomach's been bothering me again."

"You should really have it checked out. You might be getting an ulcer, Joan."

"That wouldn't be too pleasant, would it?" Joan asked. "By the way, did you hear about tthe man who swallowed a glass eye? The proctologist examined him and said, "I've been staring up assholes for twenty years, but this is the first time I've had one stare back at me.'"

Sarah laughed. Joan laughed too, And they hurried back to the unit.

"You know, I think if I ever have to watch another *Star Trek* episode I'm going to—"

"Oh, my God!" Sarah yelled. "Where's Captain Kirk?"

Sure enough, there was no sign of Dooley. "I told you to stay with him!" Joan yelled.

"You said you were going to watch him," Sarah said defensively.

"We'll talk about this later. Let's go find the maniac." Joan broke into a cold sweat. If "Captain Kirk" got loose and hurt himself she would lose her job. Neither Mackey not Clare would stand up for her then.

They quickly searched the SICU, but the captain was simply not there. They even looked in the men's bathrooms. Joan then ran into the hallway and stopped a couple of nurses. "No one's seen anything," Sarah reported.

Joan flung open the stairway door. The stairs wound upward, to the twentieth floor, and in her mind's eye she could picture the captain up on the windy roof. She was frightened at the thought, remembering the time she had gone up there to gather snow for the wine cooler for last year's Christmas party.

Sarah caught up with her on the second landing. "I'd better go call security!"

"No!" Joan said. "You're not calling anybody!" She definitely didn't want an official incident report filed.

Sarah was shocked. "Joan, pull yourself together! We have to get help."

Joan said, "You just check the rec room. I'm heading for the roof."

How did I get into this mess? she wondered. In her mind, she wanted to blame Sarah. But deep down she knew it was her own fault for having left her patient alone in the first place. As she ran huffing up the stairs she suddenly heard Sarah's triumphant yell: "Joan, I've got him!"

She hurried down the stairs into the hall and found Sarah standing outside the patients' rec room This room was used by recuperating patients from the regular floors. At eight o'clock at night it was empty.

"He's in there," said Sarah, out of breath.

Joan pushed at the door but to her amazement it wouldn't budge. "Mr. Dooley. I mean, Captain Kirk," said Joan, "this is 'Bones.'"

There was silence at the other side of the door. "Yes, what is it, Bones?" Although the pitch was higher, Dooley's voice had a strong resemblance to the "real" Captain Kirk's. He had the inflections down perfectly.

"Captain," said Joan, pressing her mouth close to the door, "I'm afraid you've contracted a very serious illness on that strange planet." Joan improvised as she went along.

"Bones," said the captain, "the entire star system depends on me."

"You told me that already, Captain," said Joan anxiously.

"I believe we've fallen into a Klingon trap."

"Maybe you're right, Captain," said Joan. "Let me come in and we can work out a plan."

There was a moment of hesitation, and then the sound of furniture scraping over wooden floors. As soon as a crack appeared, Sarah and Joan pushed open the door. Dooley had a wide grin on his face.

"Oh, my God," said Sarah. "Look at this." The room was furnished with heavy tables and chairs. In the short time he had been missing, Mr. Dooley had used his manic energy to create a furniture barricade by the door. Joan grabbed Dooley under one skinny elbow and Sarah took the other.

"Come on, Captain," said Joan. "Time to make the plan."

They guided him back to the unit. Luckily no administrators had made rounds in the last hour.

"I'll make out the incident report now," Sarah said, and turned quickly.

"Wait a minute," said Joan. "Call Bijan and get a telephone order for four-point restraints. I'll document this in the notes." Sarah was about to question whether this would be sufficient, but when she saw Joan's panicked and determined face, she thought better of it.

"I am Captain James T. Kirk on Federation business. Our mission is peaceful. But I am not prepared to accept any interference from subordinates." Dooley continued muttering on and on.

Shortly afterward Bijan came onto the floor. Other than this one murmuring man, he saw only sleeping or comatose patients. "Things are awfully quiet around here," he said. "What's the big rush on restraining Captain Kirk? Hey, Joan, do you want to hear something disappointing? I heard that what was her name?—Heather Asher—our Whipple— is back in the hospital. She was readmitted for insertion of a Broviac catheter."

"That'll make her more comfortable, at least," said Joan distractedly. "Not so many injections." She continued to work on the note.

"So, it's quiet as outer space here," said Bijan. "Admit it. You ICU nurces have it pretty easy," he said, giving a broad yawn that showed all his gold fillings. "Now, down in admitting, there's the real excitement. Your biggest problem here is how to keep from falling asleep." He pretended to be snoring, his stentorian noises blending with the heavy humming of the machines all around him.

Sarah went into the break room for a cup of tea. On the table she spotted Joan's Maalox bottle, left uncovered when they went off to search for the captain. She automatically began to screw on the cap when something struck her as suspicious. She quickly unscrewed the cap and tilted the bottle toward the sink. Instead of a chalky white antacid, out poured a colorless liquid she immediately recognized as vodka.

"Heather's not feeling sick," Norton explained to Karen. "It's just that her vein ruptured during chemo last month. Dr. Kendall felt that she'd do better with a permanent catheter. You know, that way they can give her whatever medications she needs, without waking her up if she's asleep."

The day before, Karen had been called by Ben Kendall. It was a business call: could she take the Heather Asher case? She agreed immediately and was flattered that he had thought of her, but was disappointed the call hadn't been more personal.

"I feel like the bionic woman," said Heather, laughing. "Pretty soon I'll have all plastic parts. Dr. Sanborn is such a good surgeon, I'm not worried about a thing."

"I wish I had your atttitude this early in the morning, Heather," said Karen. She was enthralled by this woman. In just the one day she had spent with Heather and Norton she had become enchanted with them both.

The door opened and in walked a young resident. He picked up the chart. "You'll be going in for surgery in a few minutes," he said. He hadn't bothered to introduce himself. He was short and curly-haired, with a self-important air about him.

Karen caught a glimpse of his badge: Robert Inwood, M.D.

"Are you an anesthesiologist?" asked Norton, who had become quite familiar with the hospital routine.

"Yes," said Dr. Inwood. "I'm a resident in that department. I work with Dr. Mackey."

"Doctor," said Karen, "Mrs. Asher hasn't received her

steroids yet this morning. Could you be sure to read my notes on that?"

"There's no time to give it now," he said. "The surgeon's already scrubbing. Don't worry," he added breezily, "we'll give them to her in the operating room. The stress of surgery sometimes makes it necessary to even increase the dose for a short period and then taper it back down."

"You won't forget?" Karen asked sweetly. He smiled condescendingly.

At nine-thirty Karen helped Heather into a clean gown. She started an IV in Heather's arm and said, "This is the last one of these you'll ever have." Karen felt happy about that.

"You think of everything, don't you?" Heather asked. Two orderlies came to take her to the OR.

"This is just routine, isn't it?" asked Norton. He was starting to get nervous. "My stomach's beginning to churn."

"No wonder. You haven't eaten anything yet, Norton," said Karen. "Let's go to the cafeteria. She won't be out for at least an hour. It'll be more pleasant to wait there."

When they returned from the cafeteria Karen went to the recovery room and found Heather just coming out of surgery. The operation had been a success. Twenty minutes later they returned her to the room. Karen helped get her into the bed, and she tried to take her temperature. Heather was too sleepy to hold the thermometer under her tongue. Karen took her pulse, which was low but consistent with anesthesia and sleep. She took her blood pressure, which also was lower than normal. Karen was mildly puzzled. Norton, however, was concerned about how pale she looked.

Fifteen minutes later Karen roused Heather and took her vital signs again. "I'm feeling so weak," said Heather. "I guess that's to be expected." Her pressure had fallen almost ten points. Half an hour later it was down another five points.

That's it for me, Karen thought. She excused herself and went out to the desk. She paged the resident, waited fifteen minutes, but there was no answer. Suddenly it hit her. She found the operating-room records. There was no entry of Heather having received her steroids. It was unlikely they would have forgotten to record it. Without steroids, Heather would most likely slip into adrenal failure and die.

When she returned to the room it was almost noon. Norton said, "She's sleeping like a baby. I think I'll go home and take a nap too. See you tomorrow. Same time, same channel."

"I'll call you later," she said, trying to mask her growing concern. "Have a nice nap." Karen had no intention of going home until her patient was stable. She feared that Heather would die of neglect if she left.

Norton walked out, without a hint of the danger his wife faced. Karen took the vital signs again and saw that the pulse and pressure were continuing to drop. She went back to the desk, pale with anger.

"Did the resident call back?" she asked the desk nurse. The young woman shook her head and so Karen got out the attending physician's phone book and called the surgeon.

"I'm sorry, Dr. Sanborn is not available. This is his answering service."

"This is the hospital calling," Karen said forcefully. She kept her voice calm, however. "There is an emergency concerning a patient he operated on. Heather Asher. Please have the doctor call me at extension 4513. This is an emergency," she repeated.

She hung up and waited. Four minutes later the phone rang. Karen spilled out her story.

"Jesus Christ. Hang a bottle of steroids, her standard

dose. I'll be right over," said Dr. Sanborn. Karen went back to the room. Heather was still asleep. Her mouth dropped open. Karen hung the bottle of medication and assembled an array of emergency equipment by the bedside in anticipation of the doctor's arrival. A few miunutes later Dr. Sanborn entered. He was a man in his late fifties, his strong, youngish face set off by white hair.

Heather had an almost immediate, positive response to the steroids. Her heart rate, pulse, and blood pressure were returning to normal.

Dr. Sanborn approached Karen outside the room. "You saved that woman's life," he said appreciatively.

"From where I stood, it looked more like you did," said Karen. "But thank you."

They chatted for a few minutes about adrenal dependency in patients receiving long-term steroid therapy. Karen was feeling good about her profession and herself. She went to the bathroom, then on her way back stopped at the nurses' station.

Residents and staff nurses crowded the area. The nurses were charting, while the doctors were sitting in their green scrubs, looking tired. Suddenly Dr. Inwood stood up.

"Hey, you!" he yelled at Karen. "Don't you *ever* call an attending physician again unless I tell you to. There is a chain of command here, and maybe you just forgot it or maybe you just don't know it."

The other nurses became silent. They stopped writing and turned toward Karen to see how she would respond. When Karen got angry, she became extremely articulate and precise.

"I generally don't respond to 'Hey, you!' " she said after a moment, "but I'll make an exception this afternoon. Your outburst makes it clear to everyone that the stress of your position is ovewhelming you." She put down the coffee cup she was holding and stepped toward him with her hand extended. "My name is Karen Bovit, R.N.," she said. "You haven't introduced yourself yet."

He glared at her, aware of all the eyes on him. Finally he touched her hand briefly and replied sarcastically, "Robert Inwood, M.D."

Karen continued in a calm, almost lilting tone of voice. "Dr. Inwood, your position in this hospital is that of a student. You are finished with medical school, and you are a doctor, but you choose to come here and do a three-year residency to continue your education. Fine. However, I am not a student, nor are the attending physicians. We are colleagues."

"You just do your nursing," he said glibly, "and cut the lecture."

Karen ignored his interruption. "One of the functions of a registered nurse," she continued, "is to observe patients and collect data. When those data indicate that medical intervention is required the nurse has to communicate with the doctors."

"Why didn't you page me?" he demanded.

"You were paged. You did not respond. And so I called Dr. Sanborn, who did. My concern is not for your status. It is for the patient. Period." She stopped.

Dr. Inwood stared, astounded. The other residents looked away, while the nurses looked as if they could hardly suppress an urge to applaud. "You had no cause . . ." Dr. Inwood offered.

"If you had read the nurses' notes, as I told you to originally, Doctor," Karen said, "none of this would have happened."

"Oh, the nurses' notes!" he said, suddenly inspired. "Why don't you go write a rank-and-file leaflet about it?

That seems like the new way to attack doctors in this hospital." He sounded like a true disciple of Dr. Mackey.

Karen stared at him angrily. "Don't blame everything on the leaflets, Doctor. Some of these problems you bring on yourself."

"Uhura, prepare for approach of the Star Fleet commander!" Mr. Dooley yelled, struggling against his ankle and wrist restraints.

"Why did they have to transfer Mr. Dooley to us anyway, Bijan?" Joan asked impatiently. "I really can't stand this anymore. It's been a week. He's psychiatric."

"Psychiatry can't handle his liver complications," said Bijan heatedly. "He's in Surgical ICU because they thought he might need an operation. Besides, what's one more lunatic up here?" He smiled at them, hooking his chubby hands into his belt.

"This isn't a joke, Bijan," Joan said. "I want him out."

Bijan became serious. "I know it's hard when the psychiatric condition interferes with treating the physical problem."

"In other words," said Joan, "you can't cure his liver problems and you can't cure his mental problem either. So you waste a bed in the SICU."

"The obvious answer would be to find a level of lithium carbonate which Mr. Dooley can tolerate, without compromising his liver function. We're working on it. If you ask me," Bijan said, lowering his voice, "someone got lithium carbonate confused with dilithium crystals," he said, laughing.

"What are we supposed to do if he gets out of hand?" Sarah asked. "After all, there's no sedative we can use."

"You'll just have to continue using four-point restraints," said Bijan. "Like in the good old days, before drugs. It'll be interesting. We'll have to get the medical students to see it."

"No wonder the poor guy feels like a prisoner of the Klingons," said Sarah sympathetically.

"I'm going to wind up in four-point restraints if he doesn't get out of here soon," Joan said without a trace of humor.

The old-fashioned Checker cab pulled up to the curb. The driver hopped out and unfolded Heather's wheelchair from the trunk. "Do you need some help?" he asked, extending his hand.

"I can walk," said Heather, but she was relieved to have Karen Bovit help her into the building.

"Norton, what have you done?" she asked. "This place must have cost a fortune. Now that I'm dying, you're finally willing to be a big spender!"

"Are you kidding?" Norton asked casually. "The doctor promised me you'd make it for the length of the lease. But no longer! If you decide to hang around we'll have to check you into a fleabag hotel!"

"Well, I'm glad to see that you're not going to baby me," she said, "just because I pulled the short straw."

Karen enjoyed this constant repartee. Most people in their condition would be terrified. The Ashers, in some strange way, seemed to be sharing another adventure. She helped Heather move from the wheelchair to the couch. The town house was furnished beautifully.

Heather was breathless from the effort. "Whew! Am I out of shape! It's not easy to get around without your insides." She sat on the couch, looking pale and pained.

"The first day home is always the most difficult, Heather," said Karen. "What we have to do is work out a progressive ambulation schedule for you."

"What a nice way of saying 'take a walk.'" She smiled. "I assume there's an elevator in this mansion," Heather continued. "I'm not much in the mood for climbing. And a kitchen?" she asked.

"Up on the fourth floor," said Norton. "It's a beaut. You should see the professional stove we've got for you."

"Do you think I'm going to be doing much entertaining, Norton?" She laughed. When she saw the hurt look on Norton's face she said, "C'mon, Norton. Why don't you show Karen the kitchen? I'll just rest here and then after lunch I'll go explore the castle."

He bent down and gave her hug.

After lunch Karen excused herself to call Ben Kendall. "I wanted you to know that I'm staying with the Ashers for as long as they want," she said.

"That's great. You can do me a big favor. Since you're there you could draw some blood for me."

"No problem," said Karen. "Do you want just a blood count, or chemistry as well?"

"Both," he said. Then he added a bit awkwardly, "I really enjoyed talking to you at Clare's party last month."

"I enjoyed it too," Karen said.

"So, how would you like to go out to dinner?"

"I'd love to," she said.

"You would? Great! Is Friday okay? Terrific," said Ben enthusiastically. "See you after work then?"

"I used to come over here when I was an intern," Ben said nervously.

"It seems, well, interesting." The place was a long, dark neighborhood tavern in a somewhat run-down part of town. The tables were small and covered with red and white checked tablecloths. A loud din of clashing pots came from the kitchen. "Well, I guess everything changes," said Ben.

"And not necessarily for the better. I hope this place is as good as it used to be. Do you like mussels?"

"Yes," she lied.

The waiter approached, belly first. Ben said, "We'd like an order of mussels, and whatever else you suggest."

"How about the calamary?"

"Fine," Ban answered for both of them.

They talked for a while about inconsequential matters. Then Ben asked, "Is it true that you were roommates with Clare Henderson?"

"Yes," said Karen. "Also Joan Fisher."

"The three of you together. That's hard to imagine," Ben said, laughing. "What were they like in those days?"

"Why are you so surprised?"

"You all seem so different," said Ben. "I know Clare pretty well, because I see her on the board. And Joan—" He laughed. "She's got quite a reputation around the hospital."

"How so?" asked Karen.

"Well . . . Let's say she's considered something of a swinger. You know about her and Mackey, don't you?"

"I've seen them together," said Karen, uncomfortable talking about her friend. "Ben, there's something I've been wanting to ask you." He looked up expectantly. "How did you get involved with the rank-and-file group?"

"Well," said Ben, "I think that nurses are the most important link in the whole system of patient care. I don't mean to sound like Albert Schweitzer, but I think we must do everything possible when sick people come to us for help. I think that patients are endangered by doctors like Phil Mackey."

Karen smiled. She had heard this sort of speech before from doctors. "That's sounds good," she said finally. "I wonder if you really know what nursing is all about?"

"I should," he said. "Ten years ago I was Benjamin W. Kendall, R.N. That's how I got through medical school. I supported myself as a private nurse. So I think I know what I'm talking about."

"I guess you do," Karen said slowly. "You know, that really surprises me."

"Sorry," said Ben. "I'll try to be more predictable in the future." They both laughed.

After dinner they walked awhile and then took a cab. At Karen's door they both felt shy.

"Did Heather or Norton ever tell you about their boat?" asked Ben suddenly. "I love that kind of adventurous spirit."

"They're such exceptional people," said Karen, agreeing. "Ben, what made you choose cancer research?" Karen was unable to mask her desire to understand Ben.

"I think it's the most interesting area of medicine," he answered automatically. His attention was clearly not on the conversation. "You know, Karen, I like you very much." Suddenly he leaned over and kissed her. She responded for a moment, then broke the embrace.

"I'll talk to you tomorrow from work," she said hurriedly. His kiss had awakened feelings in her she wasn't ready to act on.

"This is very nice," said Clare, looking around Karen's apartment. "Better than our old dorm."

"The previous tenants left a lot of nice things," said Karen modestly. "Tha antiques and the prints are mine."

"They're all lovely," said Clare, walking around and picking up a few items. "I always thought I'd love to have a place in the city someday. It won't be soon, however." She hesitated. "Did I tell you that Ken was laid off?"

"What?" asked Karen, shocked.

"Last week," Clare said, trying to sound matter-of-fact but not succeeding. "They gave him notice. It's not the first time, but we're getting fed up."

"What are you going to do now?" Karen asked.

"Who knows?" Clare said, laughing. "Construction's in a slump. Maybe I'll start moonlighting to cover Becky's dentist bills."

"I'm really sorry to hear it," said Karen. "Ken deserves better." She served hot chocolate from a beautiful white pitcher, and they both drank for a while. "I hate to add to your troubles, Clare," Karen said finally, "but I've got another problem for you."

"I figured something was on your mind," Clare said quickly. "Something to do with Ben Kendall?"

"No, it's Joan," she said.

"Her drinking again?" Clare asked immediately. Karen nodded. "I know about it. I've even spoken to her about it." She thought for a minute. "Why, has something new happened?"

"It's getting worse," Karen said. "I also spoke to her— or tried to—after your party last month. She just blew up in my face. Clare, did you know Joan lost her license last year for drunken driving?"

"My God," said Clare. "To be honest, it doesn't surprise me. People are talking about her around the hospital. One of her coworkers even came to me and confided that Joan's hung over all the time."

"I think it's worse than that," said Karen slowly. "I hate to sound disloyal—"

"Don't be silly! I have to know," Clare interjected.

"I think that Joan's getting drunk on the job. I heard that a few weeks ago she let a psychotic get loose in the SICU. He could have committed suicide. Sarah told me that Joan swigs vodka out of her Maalox bottle. I myself have seen her drinking out of that thing, but naturally I thought it was antacid."

Clare thought for a moment. "This is really serious," she said. "It could turn into a terrible embarrassment for the hospital—I mean, a terribly dangerous situation."

"Then you'll speak to her?" Karen asked optimistically.

"I don't know," Clare said carefully. "What can I do? I've already spoken to her. She's our friend, Kar'."

"Clare!" Karen said vehemently. "She may be our friend, but she's also an impaired nurse. You can force her to AA by threatening to fire her."

"Are you telling me how to do my job?" Clare asked. "How do you think it would look if I fired her? You know, I hired her—despite certain rumors then. Besides, now she's got Dr. Mackey on her side. Do you know what he'd make of this on the board? At the very least, my whole proposal for integrated notes would suffer a fatal blow."

"And your hopes of getting Charlottte's job?" Karen blurted out. It was not something she had meant to say.

Clare was taken aback for a moment. "I don't know who told you that," she said evenly. "It's not likely that Charlotte will leave. Even if she did, there would be a search committee . . ." Her voice trailed off. "It wouldn't be good news for anyone if Joan was fired. Least of all for Joan."

"What if it's the only way to get her to AA?"

"You always were filled with brilliant ideas, Kar'," Clare said, smiling. "Unfortunately, this situation may be a bit more complicated than you imagine."

# NINE

*January*

At midnight Joan met Phil Mackey in the back room of the Post Mortem.

"What's this all about?" he asked impatiently. "I've got three operations tomorrow morning."

"So what?" Joan said, slumping into her cushioned seat. "I told you, Phil. I've got to talk to you."

"All right," said Mackey. He squeezed his jaw with his hand, in an exaggerated gesture of rapt attention.

"I can't take it anymore. They put this maniac Captain Kirk in the SICU, when the man belongs in psychiatry. For a month now he's been driving me crazy. Bijan keeps promising, but he's worthless. I've talked to Clare. Nothing. I'm climbing the walls. Can't you do anything about it, Phil? I mean, I've done you enough favors in my day."

Mackey laughed uneasily. "Look, Joan, I told you—we can't mix our personal and professional lives. I sympathize with you, but you've got to swim on your own in this hospital. The fact that we're friends—"

"Oh, cut it out, Phil," she said, her voice rising. "You're

not only head of anesthesiology, you're the associate director of the whole frigging hospital. If you wanted to," she cajoled, "you could *order* him to psychiatry and that would be the end of it." She took a gulp of her drink.

"Go easy on that," Phil said nervously.

"Hey, look," she said, staring at him aggressively, "I'm a grown woman. I'll do whatever I want." There was an awkward silence: in some ways Mackey was afraid of Joan. She tried to soften the mood again. "I swear, Phil, if I didn't know better I'd say you'd been talking to Clare. Or to Karen Bovit. Hey, maybe you've been two-timing me with her," she mumbled, laughing out loud at the thought.

"Has Clare said something about your drinking?" Mackey asked, his eyes widening. "What did she say?"

"What do you care? I thought you hated her. Oh, I get it. You're scared I might create a scandal for you? Maybe I will. You deserve it for being such a bastard," she said, and her voice grew loud.

"Will you keep your voice down, for God's sake!" He pulled back his starched cuff and looked at his watch.

"I will not!" she said, her brown eyes flashing. "I'll do whatever I please, Grandpa."

"And don't call me Grandpa in public," he said, squirming uncomfortably in his seat. He cursed himself for having agreed to come out to meet her.

"Oh," she said with heavy sarcasm, "now he doesn't want to be called Grandpa." She gulped her vodka defiantly. "Does memory deceive me, or is that a different line than the one you were using when you snake-charmed me into your water bed?"

"Shut up, Joan," Mackey said, working up his courage. "You weren't exactly a virgin when I found you."

"And I'll tell you why," she said somewhat incoherently.

"Because of pricks like you!" Mackey's greatest fear was now being realized—people were staring and talking.

"This is ridiculous," said Phil grimly. He had become calmly resolute. "Listen, Joan, you're drunk. There's no point in talking to you now. I'll get a cab and take you home."

"So now you want to take me home, hunh? Wouldn't mind a little tumble in the sack?" He was embarrassed, because in the past Joan's drinking had indeed opened the door to sex. "What becomes of me, Dr. Mackey? I'm getting screwed, in every sense of that term. What's in it for me? Quickie dickie with Lackey Mackey?" She found herself hysterically funny.

Dr. Mackey now became cold and angry. One of the tortures of his childhood had been nicknames. Now, past fifty, he had to suffer that indignity all over again. Joan tried to place her empty glass on the round tabletop, but it came down with a crash, making the last ice cubes leap.

"Okay, get up," said Phil, himself standing, and trying the authoritarian approach. "I'm taking you home." Several bar patrons—one of whom Phil Mackey recognized from work—hid their smiles and he thought he heard his nickname being repeated.

"Don't be so hard on me," Joan said. "Listen, Grandpa. You know what they say. Candy is dandy, but incest is best."

Phil Mackey managed to get Joan out into the freezing early January air. The wind whipped viciously off the river and down the side streets. "Don't think I don't know what's going on, Joan," he said, pulling the collar of his camel's hair coat around his neck. He didn't bother to help her close her parka. "You've been drinking on the goddamned job." Now that they were outside he let out his frustrations, shouting at her. His voice was quickly carried away by the wind. "You little slut! You swore up and down you never did that. You're nothing but a common drunk."

Strangely, Joan didn't mind the cursing. "So what? You knew I nipped away at the ol' Maalox," Joan said, laughing. "I'm going back inside. It's cold out here. Hey, drinktender, another bar, please!" She giggled, but Phil was beyond laughter. Her voice became momentarily clearer. "I deserve to get smashed once in a while. Relieves tension. Ask Sarah if you don't believe me."

"I don't have to," said Phil with sober determination. She didn't like the look in his eye. It was menacing. Mackey glanced at his gold watch. "Okay, Joan, last chance. Do you want me to take you home?"

She shrugged her shoulders and walked silently with him to the avenue. He hailed the first cab that went by. The cab driver took one look at her and said, "Twenty dollars if she throws up in the back seat, mister."

She ignored the cab driver. "Transfer him, Phil," Joan pleaded. "Get Captain Kirk out of there. Or get me out of there. I can't stand it anymore. One or the other."

Phil thought this over. "I think it can be arranged," he said finally.

A few days later Phil Mackey left a message for Clare to meet him in the anesthesiology break room. It was a small room off the operating rooms, filled with sagging leather chairs and over-stuffed filing cabinets. It smelled mannish, and Clare felt vaguely uncomfortable there—as if she had wandered into the wrong locker room. Its one redeeming feature was the excellent pastries that appeared mysteriously every morning.

"What's the problem now, Dr. Mackey?" Clare asked. She resented Mackey summoning her onto his turf.

They were alone but Mackey spoke guardedly. "It's your

friend Joan," he said, pouring coffee into two large brown mugs.

Clare laughed uneasily. "Oh, now she's *my* friend?" she said.

"Okay, our friend," he conceded. "I'm worried about her, Clare, and I think you know what I'm talking about."

"Which is—?"

Mackey looked annoyed. He had wanted her to bring it up first. "Which is her drinking problem. I'm sure it hasn't escaped your notice that Joan has been drinking more and more lately. The other night she summoned me out into the cold to meet her at the Post Mortem. It was hardly midnight, but she was already plastered."

"So?" asked Clare. She was stalling for time. Time to think.

"Don't play dumb with me, Clare. The woman got off of work at eleven. She'd been drinking on the job. That's inexcusable behavior in an SICU nurse."

Clare gnawed her bottom lip nervously, then stopped suddenly when she realized she was doing it. "I'm aware that Joan has some problems," she said cautiously. "I'm not aware that she's drinking on the job, Phil. . . . What are you suggesting I do?" she added, trying to figure out what Mackey's game was.

"You're her friend, as well as the associate director of nursing. Someday you may be director of nursing." He smiled conspiratorially. "I don't want to interfere in the personnel problems of your department. But you know what I would do if this were one of my residents."

"What's that?" asked Clare. She felt slightly ill talking this way.

"Do I have to draw you a picture?" he asked, opening his palms to her. Clare took a big gulp of coffee, then lifted her eyes and stared into his. "Get rid of her," he said, so low she wasn't sure she heard him.

"Fire her?" Clare asked. She wanted to sound indignant, but she couldn't help it: her voice came out exactly like his. "Just like that? I thought you were her friend, Phil," she added sarcastically.

"I am, of course," he said easily. "But this is business. This girl can screw things up for both of us," he said.

Especially you, she was about to say, but checked herself. "What a situation," said Clare, sighing.

"She's made a mess of things. It's her own fault. One way or the other, I'm finished with her. It would be best for everyone if you'd just handle her quietly," he added.

Joan had been close to this man, Clare thought, but he wouldn't stand by her the minute her behavior threatened his position. Joan was becoming a major embarrassment to her as well. She hated to think of herself as no better than Phil Mackey.

"I'd have to conduct an investigation, of course."

"A private investigation." He nodded. "It's sad," he added, standing up, "but we have to always protect Riverview's good name."

"Well, thank you for telling me all this," Clare said coldly, and put down her barely touched coffee.

"Don't let this slide, Clare," Mackey said. "Because if you do, someone else will have to handle her. And they might not be so kind."

Clare walked into the dining room of her house. "Hi, everybody! I'm home!" She pulled off her gloves and blew on her hands. The ride from the station was not long enough to warm the car.

She heard a muffled cry. "Be right up!" Ken was in the basement, and she could see the light through the floorboards. He came up covered with grease and dirt. "You won't believe the day I've had," he said, laughing. "Wouldn't you know, the boiler picked just this day to conk out. I went all over the county looking for a part. This machine isn't made anymore."

She leaned over and kissed him, trying not to get any dirt on her blue woolen suit. "Am I hungry," she said.

Ken looked embarrassed. "Look, I'm sorry," he began. "We'll have to go out to eat. I didn't have a chance to put anything up."

"Couldn't you have at least popped a frozen meal in the oven, Ken?" she asked. Clare hated to be the nagging wife, especially when Ken was unemployed.

"I just explained," he said, "I was all over creation looking for a valve." There was a soccer ball lying in the doorway. "I've told Kenny a thousand times not to leave his stuff in here." He kicked the ball. It flew with surprising velocity and rebounded with a sharp crack off the wall. Until that moment he hadn't known he was so angry.

"Okay," Clare said, deliberately remaining calm. "Why don't you take Kenny and run down to the chicken place? I'll throw together some vegetables." She put up frozen peas and corn and was shredding carrots for a salad when the doorbell rang. With a sigh she answered it. Nancy Taylor stood there, panting.

"Come on in," Clare said, trying to hide her annoyance. What a time to come visiting!

"Hi, Clare," said Nancy. "Are you eating?"

"No, you can help me cut up these carrots. Ken went to get some fried chicken." Nancy was glad to help, and as they worked they continued to talk.

"I'm really worried about Stephanie," Nancy said.

"I am too," said Clare quickly. "What's happened? Has she gotten worse?"

"Today she had diarrhea again," said Nancy, hardly able to control her shaking voice. "Her fever was up to 101, until I broke down and gave her two aspirin."

"Nancy, did you ever follow up on those tests Dr. Kendall recommended?" She thought she knew the answer.

"No, Clare, I've just been so busy taking care of Stephanie," said Nancy apologetically.

"Obviously the problem hasn't gone away, Nancy. I think you'd better find the time." Clare couldn't help being annoyed. She and Ben had spoken to Nancy at length at the party. Ben had told her, "Any infection that doesn't go away after such a long time has to be taken very seriously." Nancy was clearly running away from the problem.

"I'm so worried," Nancy said suddenly. "You know, you read all sorts of things."

"What sorts of things?" asked Clare. She wanted to see how much Nancy knew or suspected.

"All sorts of horrible things," she repeated, trying to fight back tears with an out-of-place smile. "I'll take her in first thing next week."

"Well, I spoke to Clare," Nancy Taylor said when she had dashed back to her house through the crusty snow.

"What did she say?" Bill Taylor asked. He had a long-standing grudge against the Hensons because Ken had once turned the hose on his dog. He hated to turn to them for help.

"She thinks Steph had better have more tests at Riverview." She paused. "She's losing weight again," Nancy added.

"What are you suggesting?" Bill asked, panicky. "It's just an infection, dear. We've had perfectly good doctors examine her, and they've said—"

"I've lost my faith in doctors," Nancy said a bit

hysterically. "At least in these doctors," she added. "We'd better go talk to Stephanie."

Upstairs they found their daughter asleep, a pencil in her hand. Stephanie was in the middle of a book of word-find puzzles. She awoke as soon as they entered. "I'm feeling sick again, Ma." Stephanie's voice came weakly.

Her mother reached for her daughter's forehead. The fever was back again. Suddenly Stephie let loose with a rasping cough, choking on the liquid in her lungs.

"I wanted to help make the bread," Stephanie said.

"Some other time, darling," said Nancy. She took a wet washcloth and gently dabbed at Stephanie's warm face. "Steph," said her mother, "we have to talk to you." She sat down gingerly on an antique toy chest catty-corner in the room, picking up one of Stephanie's dolls and absent-mindedly straightening its hair. Her father sat on the edge of the bed and tickled her. She made an effort to laugh as she had in the old days.

"You're going to let me bake, aren't you, Ma? I could bundle up."

"Darling, I was just talking to Clare Henson. She thinks you should go for some more tests at Riverview."

"I hate those tests," Stephanie said. Just last week Stephanie had refused to go to the city for tests, and Nancy had gone along out of pity for her child. This evening, however, Stephanie did not seem so opposed to the idea. "Would they prick my finger again? It hurts when they squeeze your finger like that."

"Steph," said her father gently, "I'm sure it won't be that bad. We have to do something. We can't go on like this. And remember, you did agree that after New Year—"

"All right," Stephanie said suddenly. "I can't stand being sick anymore. I'll do whatever you say, if I can get better." She thought for a minute. "Do you think Clare's friend Joan could take care of me?"

"Do you want her to?" asked Nancy.

"Yes!" said Stephanie. "She was so nice!"

"How does herpes leave the hospital?" Joan asked, smiling tensely. She, Clare, and Karen were walking in the garden of the hospital, which towered over the river drive. It was a clear sunlit afternoon, crisply cold. They all wore their winter coats buttoned up to the neck.

Clare stared across at her for a long moment. "Okay, I guess I don't have any choice. Tell me: how *does* herpes leave the hospital?"

"On crotches!"

Karen, who had stopped to lean against the rusty railing, turned and laughed. Clare smiled wanly. "Very good, Joan," she said patronizingly.

"Ready for another one?" asked Joan excitedly. "The Pope dies and goes to heaven . . ."

"Listen, Joan," Clare said abruptly, "what we've got to talk to you about is no joke."

"My, my," said Joan nervously, "aren't we serious?"

"We do have some serious things to discuss," said Karen, exhaling her visible breath into her hands.

"I thought it would be better for us all to meet here," Clare added, "so we could have some privacy."

"Can we make it quick? I'm freezing my ass off. And listen, if this is about Captain Kirk," said Joan hurriedly, "I can explain it without all this rigamarole. I know that as the SICU supervisor," beginning a speech she had rehearsed in her mind, "I bear responsibility for what goes on in my unit. I hoped it wouldn't come to this, but Sarah left her post at the wrong moment. In my opinion, that's what caused him to get loose. I didn't file a report because no harm was done. What's the big deal?"

Clare looked over at Karen, exasperated, then turned back. "Look, Joan, I don't know what you're talking about, and I'm not sure I want to know. What I have to talk to you about is more serious. I've had a number of reports now that you've been drinking on the job."

Joan looked positively stunned. Then her face lit up. "Mackey!" she said derisively. "He's an idiot! The man's hung up on me. He has a definite problem." Her face colored as she went on, nervously. "What's behind this is as follows. We had a big fight last week. The reason was that I wasn't in the mood. . . . So he cooked up this thing about drinking, you see?" She appealed for their sympathy with her eyes.

"Dr. Mackey may have an attitude problem, Joan," said Karen, grabbing an opening, "but you've got a drinking problem, and that's what we've got to discuss."

Joan jolted back, her expression skeptical. "I don't know what you're talking about, Kar'. A drinking problem—me?"

There was silence—except for the cawing sea gulls and the steady hum of the traffic below. Clare said as gently as she could, "Stop denying it, Joan. It's become quite visible to everyone."

"What are you talking about, Clare?" Joan asked, wheeling to face her friends. She was feeling quite surrounded.

Clare said, taking a deep breath, "What Karen said is perfectly clear. You have a drinking problem and now we have to deal with it. You've become a menace to yourself and to the patients." This came out more harshly than Clare intended, but she didn't care. The die was cast.

"This is ridiculous," said Joan, coloring. "Where do the

two of you come off to dictate to me about my personal life?"

"Let's look at the facts, Joan," Karen said, undeterred. "You lost your driver's license—"

"I knew you'd throw that up in my face!" Joan said with genuine passion. "I knew it in the car! I haven't heard the last of this, I told myself. So what's the matter, Karen," she said with childish sarcasm, "don't you have a patient to occupy your every waking moment? No substitute boyfriends to take the part of the real one you can't seem to get—"

Karen looked away. Clare was furious and intervened by taking hold of Joan's arm.

"You just let go of me!" Joan screamed, pulling away violently.

"Clare, why don't you just give her the choices?" Karen spoke quietly but with a vindictiveness that later disturbed and surprised her, when she ran over the scene in her mind.

"What is she talking about?" Joan asked angrily. "You guys sound like the cops."

Clare sighed. "One choice, Joan, would be to fire you."

Joan smiled grimly. "For what? I haven't even had one write-up, much less the three required by the personnel handbook."

"Read the handbook again, Joan. There's a clause in there about extreme circumstances. Drinking on the job is an extreme circumstance. I've done it before. I can do it again."

"What about the employee review board?" Joan asked a bit uncertainly. The hospital had instituted a review board to ward off a union drive some years before.

Clare shrugged. Everyone—Joan included—knew this was a puppet of the administration. Joan stared at them hatefully, her eyes narrowing dramatically. Finally Clare looked away.

Karen decided to try again. "Joan, you're missing the point," she said softly. "You need help."

"What do *you* think we should do?" Clare asked Joan.

"Nothing! Because I've done nothing wrong. Of all people"—her voice quavered—"I wouldn't have expected this of you two. I see I've misjudged you, so if you want to fire me, go ahead. See if you can make it stick."

"I'm willing to take the flak, Joan," said Clare, smiling slightly out of nervousness. "But I don't think there'll be any. You've got quite a reputation."

Suddenly the dam broke. Joan burst into sobs. Clare was glad that they had decided to have this meeting in the deserted, snow-filled garden. Joan cried for a long time, and when she looked up her nose was fiery red. Karen handed her a tissue, and she blew her nose noisily. Clare and Karen exchanged glances. They both hoped this meant Joan would now see things their way.

"Look, why don't you leave me alone?" she said huskily, without looking at her friends. "I'm not harming anyone. You guys are ganging up on me." Her voice broke, and she blew again, tearing what was left of the tissue to shreds. "I know I've been acting weird. But you have to understand, I'm under a lot of stress. I can't handle these psychos."

Karen, seizing the opportunity, said, "Maybe you need a break from the unit?"

"Maybe I do," she admitted.

"Maybe?" Clare asked.

"All right. Definitely. I definitely need a break. But that's no reason to fire me, is it? I mean, I've put in good service at Riverview, haven't I? And I've tried to be a good friend to you both." Although her voice was more composed, inside she was raging against the two of them. She could see exactly where this conversation was leading and hated them for it. "Well, haven't I?" she demanded.

"Sure, you have," said Karen, "and we're trying to be good friends to you."

"Please don't talk about firing me then, okay?" She looked over at Clare, her tear-filled brown eyes pleading with her friend.

"I'll tell you what," Clare said, moving closer to Karen. "We've given this a lot of thought, and there is a way out." Joan felt panic at the price she knew she'd have to pay. "I'll grant you a month's leave of absence, after which time you can resume your job." She paused. "On one condition."

Joan sarcastically filled in, "That condition will be that I go to AA meetings for the rest of my natural life."

Karen said quietly, "Joan, you're an alcoholic. Alcoholics Anonymous has helped a lot of people who want to stop drinking."

"I am not an alcoholic," said Joan, laughing defiantly. "Alcoholics have to go to meetings. I don't have to go to meetings!"

"You do now," said Clare.

"AA?" asked Joan, dismayed. "I'm not a wino! I'm a social drinker. That's a long way from the gutter."

"You've got the wrong idea about AA, Joan," Clare said. "Most people there are not coming from the gutter, they're just like you."

"And if I refuse to go?" Joan asked. She felt desperate, but her fierce anger could find no outlet.

"If you refuse I'm going to have to fire you," said Clare with cold determination.

"Joan," Karen exclaimed, "don't you see? This could be a really positive change in your life!"

"What do you know about life? You just exist." She

turned to Clare. "You'd really fire me?" she asked incredulously.

Clare nodded. "I'd also try to get your R.N. license pulled," she added without rancor.

Karen joined in. "Drunks should not take care of sick people. They are sick people themselves. It's that simple, Joan."

" 'It's that simple,' " Joan repeated—but her mimicry fell flat. "You know, I really hate you for cornering me like this. Because most of this so-called problem is in your own minds."

Karen ignored her hostility. "Now that you know your choices, what are you going to do?"

A cold gust of winter wind hit them full blast. Karen shivered.

"I don't have any choice, do I? When would I have to start this?" Joan asked finally.

"You could start on Monday morning," said Karen. "I called a friend at St. Barnabas and they have an opening in their residential program."

"I see you two have been hard at work plotting this whole thing out," Joan said. "You think of everything, little Miss Goody Two-Shoes."

"I take it this means you'll go?" asked Clare.

"Would I have to live there?" she asked with obvious disgust.

"Yes," said Clare. "It's not a prison, though. We'll both come and visit you."

"Terrific," Joan said finally. A long silence stretched between the three friends as they walked back to the hospital. Joan walked ahead, as if anxious to put the whole encounter behind her. She felt an almost bottomless anger stemming from this betrayal. So many people had let her down over the years. In the past few months she had come to look on Karen and Clare as somehow different. Now they too had turned on her. She knew she had no choice. "Okay, I'll try it," she said flatly. She continued to walk ahead of the two of them.

Karen, for her part, had a terrible premonition that their friendship was over. Joan's comments had stung her. Clare had escaped the brunt of Joan's vicious attacks. Karen felt terribly misunderstood by Joan. She really had hoped Joan would react with insight and understanding. Upon reflection, the bitterness of Joan's acquiescence bothered her. Never get between a drunk and her bottle!

Clare felt terrible when she returned to the office, brushing the snow from her coat. She was stunned by the resistance Joan had put up. She had expected the whole business to be much less uncomfortable.

Joan had left without even saying good-bye, and Karen seemed near tears. Clare had tried to convince her that the attacks would have been directed at her, too, if she wasn't the "Boss."

Betty looked startled as she came in and deleted whatever was on the computer screen.

"How's the novel coming?" Clare asked evenly.

"Hunh? What novel?"

"Oh, what a shame," Clare said with mock pity. "All that immortal prose down the drain."

"So, how'd it go with Miss Kamchatka Vodka?" asked Betty.

Clare stared at her angrily. "Are you eavesdropping on my conversations again?" she asked.

"Before I forget, you had an urgent call from Nancy Taylor. Something about her daughter Stephanie. She said she's in the emergency room."

"Here? At Riverview?"

"None other," said Betty.

"I'd better get down there right away," said Clare.

The emergency room was crowded and stuffy. It took Clare a few seconds to find Nancy and Stephanie. Clare embraced her neighbor and kissed Stephanie on the forehead. "What are you doing here?" she asked.

"Dr. Barnes told me to meet her here," said Nancy anxiously. Dr. Sheila Barnes was the head of pediatric oncology and a friend of Ben Kendall's. "When I got here the resident wanted to put Stephanie on a cancer floor!" Clare saw her friend was panicky.

"Calm down, Nancy," she said. "Pull yourself together. How are you feeling, Stephanie?"

"Okay," she answered feverishly.

"Why would they want to admit her to oncology? That's cancer, isn't it?"

Clare pulled Nancy out of earshot. "Stephanie's infection is so strange they probably want to test her for every possibility."

"What kind of possibilities?" Nancy asked. "What are you talking about?"

Just then Dr. Sheila Barnes approached. She was a tall attractive brunette. "Hello, Mrs. Taylor." She nodded greetings to Clare. "Sorry I'm late. . . ."

"Doctor, there's been a terrible mistake," said Nancy. "The resident is trying to put Stephanie on a cancer floor." Clare and Sheila exchanged glances.

Stephanie piped up. "Do I have cancer?"

Sheila Barnes laughed gently. "I don't think so, Stephanie. But they have lots of special machines up there that will help us find out what's wrong with you."

Stephanie seemed more reassured by this than her mother. Clare sensed that the doctor wanted to talk to Nancy alone. "Nancy," she said, "I'm going to take Stephanie upstairs now. Dr. Barnes will bring you up in a little while." Clare took Stephanie to the patient elevator and put her in a wheelchair. She had her laughing happily by the time the doors opened.

"Mrs. Taylor, there's no easy way to say this," said Sheila Barnes. "I'm sorry I wasn't here earlier to explain. You should understand that your daughter's symptoms are not inconsistent with a diagnosis of AIDS." The color drained from Nancy's face. Dr. Barnes guided her to a chair, and the two women sat down.

"AIDS? How is that possible? She's just a little girl. Are you sure?"

"I didn't say Stephanie *has* AIDS, Mrs. Taylor. I just want you to know what our concerns are. The transfusion she had when she broke her arm makes it necessary for us to rule out that diagnosis."

"Then she might not have it!" said Nancy desperately.

"That's right. We don't know what it is. Right now we're going to concentrate on getting rid of her pneumonia. The sophisticated test to rule out AIDS should be completed within a few weeks."

"My God! I can't believe this." She thought of her daughter with Clare. "Does Stephanie have to be told this?"

"Unless Stephanie asks directly, the issue will never be raised," said Dr. Barnes. "If she does ask, the staff will get in touch with you and your husband."

Nancy Taylor took a moment to try to digest what she had just heard. "Can I see my little girl now?" she said finally. When they reached her room Mrs. Taylor blurted out, "I hope to God she never asks!"

# TEN

## February

Norton met Karen at the door as she came in on a raw Monday morning.

"Hi, Norton," she said. "How's Heather feeling?"

"She's fine," Norton said, taking her heavy coat. "It's terrible out there." Something seemed vaguely distracted in Norton's attitude. Karen followed him into the living room, where Heather was propped up on the sofa. She did indeed look content.

"Here, Heather," said Karen. "I brought you the morning paper." Heather especially enjoyed getting the paper each morning. She took it from Karen and handed Norton the sports section. He accepted it but didn't glance at it.

"You know, Karen," he said abruptly when she returned with coffee and an English muffin, "there's something we've been meaning to talk to you about."

Karen was taken aback. After the confrontation with Joan, they were no longer speaking to each other. Without Joan as a companion, she had begun to leave for home later and later in the evenings. It would have been nice to spend more time with Clare, but realistically that was impossible. As was her style, she had become increasingly involved with Heather and Norton. In the beginning Karen had agreed to work six days a week. In practice she not only stayed late but had begun to work seven days. She enjoyed her work so much—and this case in particular—that it didn't faze her in the least. In fact it was giving structure to her life.

"Anything wrong?" she asked worriedly, glancing from one to the other.

"Nothing, dear, really," Heather reassured her. "It's just that we were thinking . . ."

"We were thinking that you need some time off," said Norton, smiling awkwardly.

"Why don't you let me decide that?" Karen said. "I'm not doing anything else, and I enjoy being here with you two. In fact I worry about you when I'm not here. I really do."

"I'm sure you do," Heather said kindly.

"We think you're wonderful," said Norton. "It's only . . . I don't know how to say this. But we feel we have to learn to stand on our own feet a little bit. Heather and I have to be more self-reliant."

"I didn't know I was interfering," she said abruptly. Then, after a brief pause, "I'm sorry, I didn't mean to snap at you. I'm just a little tired," she added.

"That's the other thing," said Norton seriously. "You're working too hard. You're here all the time. And you're not just a nurse. You're like a devoted daughter."

"Why do I get the funny feeling I'm being fired?" Karen asked, with a short laugh.

"Absolutely not!" said Norton, horrified. "But we would like you to take the rest of the week off. And we could use a little privacy."

"I guess you're right," Karen said, sighing. "And I am exhausted. "She paused. "Are you sure you'll be all right?" she asked, looking from one to the other.

"There's no problem," said Norton calmly. "I have everything in hand."

Karen slept till past nine on the following morning. She then got up and spent a lazy day in the department stores in midtown. She had lunch and bought herself a beautiful new love seat for her living room. Before she knew it, it was five o'clock, and dark. The lights in the theater district beckoned. She had some money in her pocket, time stretched in front of her, and she was free. Karen stopped in front of a telephone and lifted the receiver, unsure who to call.

Her first impulse was to call Heather and Norton and see how they were doing, but she ruled that out. She started to dial Ben's number but hung up before she completed the call. Instead she walked up the avenue and went into an old movie house, now divided into eight claustrophobic sections. Karen wasn't amused by the comedy; she felt alone and aimless. She got up carefully and left before the movie was over, grabbed a cab, and was asleep before ten.

Early the next morning, Karen went on call for a short-term case. The registry immediately called her back and assigned her a relief case for the rest of the week. By 7:30 A.M. she was sitting in the nurses' station on Astor Three, studying Kermit Newall's chart.

At first glance the case seemed quite straightforward. Newall was fifty-five. He had had ulcerating leg infections as a result of his late-onset diabetes. His doctor had given him courses of antibiotics, in ever increasing doses. The condition had only gotten worse. Finally he called in a surgeon who recommended immediate amputation. Mr. Newall had adamantly refused.

His refusal to have surgery was seen as life-threatening,

and a psychiatrist was called in on the case. In the meantime they continued to try antibiotic therapy, which had failed. Again they recommended amputation and again the patient refused, this time even more vociferously. The Riverview doctors therefore scheduled two more weeks of antibiotics in an intravenous drip, not because they really believed it would do anything but simply so they could say that everything possible had been done.

According to the notes, Mr. Newall had another problem: acute insomnia. The man had not slept more than forty-five minutes at a stretch since he came to Riverview, Karen read. His wife said he had not slept at home for several weeks before he was admitted. Dr. Leslie Talbot, a psychiatrist, was of the opinion that Newall's insomnia came from his fear of death—the fear of never waking up again.

Kermit Newall's regular private nurse, Bob Fold, had flown home for an uncle's funeral. He was supposed to be back within a day or two. Nevertheless, Karen was already becoming intrigued by Newall's problems. She remembered having seen a book about insomnia in the medical library's "Recent Acquisitions" section and made a mental note to look for it after work.

Although she was early, Karen approached Newall's room. She was anxious to meet him. From the record he seemed like a fascinating man—"a successful business-man," Dr. Talbot had said, "and definitely with a mind of his own." On the door of the room was taped an envelope with the words RELIEF NURSE written in neat letters. She opened it and read:

*Dear Relief Nurse,*

The following are some helpful hints on the routine I have established with Mr. Newall. This is day 29 of his hospitalization, and my first day off in all that time!

8:00–8:30: coffee and cigarettes (for him, not you)
9:00: call his wife
9:30: breakfast.
10:00: vital signs and medicine
12:00: VS and medicine
1:00: lunch
1:30–2:30: psychiatrist visit. Relax.
2:30–3:00: wife and/or social worker visits
3:00–4:00: VS, medicine, chart, and watch that clock!

Good luck,
Bob

That was really a nice touch, Karen thought. With such a list, taking care of Mr. Newall should be a lot easier. She made a mental note to do the same thing the next time she had a relief nurse on one of her long cases.

When Karen opened the door to the room, however, her stomach sank. Mr. Kermit Newall was sitting in an easy chair, piled high with pillows. He was wearing a hospital gown. One arm was exposed. It had the antibiotic IV drip in it. The other was enclosed in an old silk robe.

The first thing she noticed was how dirty her new patient was. His scalp, exposed within a tonsure of hair, was scabby and scaly-looking. His hair itself was greasy and stringy; gray-brown, dull, old-man hair. His legs were open to her view and had red weepy wounds. A wet dressing was draped over the bigger ulcerations.

In his chart she had read the doctors' strict orders that his legs be elevated at all times. Kermit Newall had obviously pushed away the footstool, and his feet now rested on the floor. The man's toes and feet were black and dirty. Karen was reminded of the feet of homeless derelicts. The bed, however, was clean and untouched, and positioned so that his legs would be elevated—if he used it. She felt a mixture of pity and anger. Her anger was directed at the hospital, and especially at Bob Fold, for letting his patient's hygiene deteriorite in this way.

"Good morning, Mr. Newall," she said, trying to be cheerful. "My name is Karen Bovit. I'm going to be your nurse today."

She was on the verge of offering her hand when she noticed his: the fingernails were long and had begun to curl. They looked as if they had dried feces under them. His right hand had yellow-brown nicotine stains that spoke of years, not just months, of uncleanliness.

The most disturbing thing about Kermit Newall, however, was his face. With a different expression, he might have looked like a craggy old fisherman. But Mr. Newall was neither poor nor honest. He stared at her with protruding bloodshot eyes from behind a bulbous nose. This was a hostile face, full of pain, anger, and contempt.

Newall said nothing to return her greeting. Evaluating her for a second, he rasped, "Girly, get me my cigarettes and some coffee. Now!"

Karen stared at him and her temples throbbed. She went to the counter top, freed a pack of cigarettes from the carton, and poured him a cup of black coffee. She was so astonished that she failed to make a quick rejoiner.

"Look," she said finally, "unless you want me to call you 'old man,' or worse, I suggest you refrain from calling me 'girly.' My name is Karen Bovit. If you prefer I'll respond to 'nurse.'"

Newall lit his cigarette; his yellowed hand was shaking so that he could hardly line up the match with the tip. Karen wasn't about to help him. He then sucked in the smoke greedily and held it long in his lungs with a look of total satisfaction on his face. Suddenly, as she bent over him, he exhaled a full blast of the smoke in her face. Karen recoiled, not just from the smoke but from the stench of his breath. His mouth smelled of old cavities. God knows when he brushed his teeth last, she thought.

Amused, Kermit poured some black coffee down his throat. "You *prefer,*" he said, squinting up at her angrily. "What I 'prefer' "—he mimicked—"is that you just shut up."

Tight-lipped, Karen turned around abruptly and walked out to the nurses' station. She was startled to see Linda Martinez, a friend from St. Barnabas, there.

"Linda, what are you doing here? I didn't even know you were working at Riverview," Karen said.

Linda laughed easily. She was a pert young Filipina. "Hey, Karen, how are you doing?" she asked. "Just started a month or two ago. What patient do you have?"

"Gee, Linda, it's so nice to see you again. I have Kermit Newall."

"Kermit the Hermit?" asked Linda.

Karen tried to laugh. "Do you know he told me to shut up and called me 'girly'?"

"You shouldn't mind," said Linda. "He calls all the nurses 'girly,' except for Bob Fold. He gets called worse! I heard about the way you laid into Mackey's resident, Bob Inwood! You know, Karen, that story was all over the hospital. So what did you say back to Kermit?"

"I didn't say anything. It's funny, but I find the guy intimidating. Even in his miserable state, he's still quite a bully."

"Do you mind if I give you a word of advice? Go easy with him. He's bad news."

"What do you mean?"

"Well, they say he's loaded," said Linda, lowering her

voice. "Has a seat on the stock exchange or something," she said. "We complain, but he gets away with murder because he's so filthy rich. They say the administration's expecting a Kermit Newall Memorial Wing one of these days. I think they're dreaming. Why don't you just sign off the case, Karen?" she said sympathetically.

"Thanks, Linda, but I couldn't do that to Bob Fold," she said. "I came to work and I'll stay. I'll give my eight hours a go."

"Maybe by the end of the day you'll be telling me this is the greatest case you ever worked on!" Linda teased. Karen blushed slightly. She went back into the room, wondering if this opinion of her had spread all over the hospital.

"Mr. Newall," she said, trying to start all over, "I have just been reviewing the doctors' instructions and it would be to your benefit if you would at least let me put your legs up on the footstool."

His eyes lit on Karen for a brief moment and then resumed darting around the room. "No," he said finally. What she found especially frustrating was that she recognized a keen intelligence behind his bulging eyes. Ignoring him for the moment, Karen assembled all the leg dressing supplies and returned to where he was sitting. She put everything out neatly on the over-bed table. When she had gotten everything ready to dress his legs, Mr. Newall took his cane and, without warning, knocked everything onto the floor with one well-aimed swipe. A bowl of hydrogen peroxide, a bottle of iodine solution, sterile gauze, gloves—everything broken, splattered, ruined. Mr. Newall was huffing from the effort but gave a small, self-satisfied smile of approval and then looked away.

"Okay, Mr. Newall," Karen said, breathing deeply. "It is now nine in the morning. You have already succeeded in making me very angry. Very angry! Let me tell you what my job is here today. I have a legal and moral obligation to render a service to you to the best of my ability. And as part of that service I will execute the instructions left by your doctors." She gestured theatrically to the mess on the floor. Angry, she was becoming verbose.

"If you choose, through words or actions, to refuse medical treatment, then my responsibility is to record that in the chart and notify your doctor. I don't want to tell you what to do or what to decide," she said, trying to sound reasonable. "The choice is yours. But while you are deciding," she added, "I want you to reflect on what I am saying to you. It has been my experience that maintaining and promoting good hygiene makes a person feel better. Being clean and washed can relax a body so that the mind can drift off to sleep. Your wounds would have a better chance of healing if you would let me dress them. Wouldn't you agree, Mr. Newall?"

Kermit Newall wasn't listening to her lecture. He sat with an impassive, disdainful expression on his wrinkled face. Then, suddenly, without warning, his face cracked into a cold smile. "Are you done?"

"Yes, I'm done," said Karen.

"Good. Now I want you to sit down and shut up, girly," he said with calm authority. "If I want anything else I'll tell you. Right now, just shut up."

Karen was enraged. She walked out of the room. On her way back to Astor Three, Karen stopped and made an appointment to meet Clare for lunch in the cafeteria. She returned to find Kermit with his eyes closed but not asleep—he opened them defiantly as soon as she entered. Karen remembered Mrs. Beecher, her nursing instructor, saying that "the most difficult patient is the greatest nursing challenge." She momentarily enjoyed a mental picture of frail Mrs. Beecher down on her hands and knees, trying to clip the dirty toenails of Kermit Newall!

The supplies were still all over the floor where Kermit had knocked them. Karen brought in the garbage can and a mop from the hallway and started to clean up the mess. Newall studied her for a minute. "What a dirty job you have," he said suddenly.

Karen gave him what she called her "passive aggressive" smile. "Providing the patient with a safe, clean environment is part of my professional responsibility," she said in an almost servile voice. After she had the mess cleaned up she sat down in a side chair by the bed. She was still simmering from the insults, but "passive aggressive" smiling was the least damaging expression of her anger. There was silence. I should have brought a book, she thought. At 10 A.M. his breakfast tray finally arrived. She put it on the over-bed table, within her patient's reach.

"Take off the plate cover."

"Mr. Newall. You have two good hands." She smiled. "Surely you don't want me to feed you."

With that Mr. Newall grabbed the whole tray and threw it at her. Karen leaped up just in time but remained frozen until the last dish had stopped rattling and rolling. "Mr. Newall, I understand you're a wealthy man. I'm glad, because if even one of those items had hit me I would sue you for assault and win the case."

She turned again and left the room. Linda was not at the station. Karen grabbed the chart and wrote an angry note in an attempt to dissipate her growing rage. Everyone had heard stories about abusive nurses, but what about abusive patients? she wondered. In her heart she felt she would be totally justified if she put on her coat and walked off the job now. She knew Linda and the other nurses would understand. The day was only beginning. She charted like a lawyer, then returned to the room and began silently to pick up the latest mess.

"Girly," said Newall slowly, "didn't I tell you you have a dirty job?" He seemed to derive some peculiar pleasure from humiliating her. When she refused to reply he said sarcastically, "Let me tell you what *I* see as your job. You job is to do what *I* say. And *I* think you should ask permission before you leave this room. You were gone over half an hour last time!" He paused and then continued in his regular voice. "That is, if you expect to get paid by me."

Karen could no longer control herself. "Listen," she said, "I don't intend to be provoked into lowering my standards by arguing with such a slimy, scuzzy, low-life as you!" She stopped, out of breath and feeling there was an unreal, almost nightmarish quality to the moment. She was not used to losing control in front of anyone, much less a patient. Yet he had provoked her into stooping to his level. She returned to cleaning with a furious energy.

Mr. Newall was not dissuaded. Quite the opposite. "Girly, you are disgusting. Now get me a cigarette and then sit in your chair until I am ready for you to clean up the mess you made."

All right, Karen thought, this is war! "Mr. Newall, there is no smoking allowed in the patients' rooms by order of the fire marshal." Play on his nicotine hunger, she thought; cruel but effective.

Newall tried not to show any anxiety. "Girly, maybe you don't know who I am. I have given Riverview Hospital not thousands, not tens of thousands, but *millions* of dollars! I don't think the doctors are going to be very happy with the report I'm intending to give them on you." Karen smiled but continued to ignore him. Newall waited a full minute, then screamed, "Get me a cigarette!"

Thank God for nicotine fits, Karen thought maliciously.

She got up and slowly closed the door. She smiled her little passive smile and said, "If you continue to yell, you will upset the other patients. And I know you're too kind to be insensitive to the needs of others."

"That's it! You're a sadist and you're fired."

Karen smiled. "Your psychiatrist will be here today at one-thirty, and so if you feel the need to act out your aggressions or display any delusions of grandeur, please wait until then. Dr. Talbot might benefit from seeing your outbursts."

Newall pursed his lips and closed his eyes. Karen bent down to pick up a hard roll that had fallen a few feet in front of him, but it was the wrong move. Suddenly she felt a blinding flash of pain and heard a loud noise. The mortification came next. For, as she bent over, Kermit had grabbed his cane and hit her with it full force across her back.

No serious damage had been done, but Karen momentarily lost control. She stood up and grappled the cane out of his bony hands. His strength was surprising. She lifted it high in the air. It came whoosing angrily down, landing on the footrest just inches from his scabby leg, and raising a cloud of dust. Again she raised the stick and brought it down with surgical precision on the other side of the leather hassock.

Kermit shrank away from her, petrified, as she beat the sides of the footstool with loud smacking noises. "That's it, mister," she snarled through her clenched teeth. "Don't you dare open your mouth, and don't make one false move," she said in her best John Wayne manner, "or I'll throw your body out of that chair and tell everyone you had a little accident." Her anger was real, but from the first blow she had calculated it for maximum effect. This was mainly an educational exercise for Kermit Newall, although probably not what kindly Mrs. Beecher had in mind when she spoke of patient education! Karen didn't care anymore. She was now in total control of the situation and herself, and had no desire to do the "right" thing.

When her anger had spent itself she had a wonderful revelation. She now knew that she had the means to do whatever she wanted to Mr. Newall. And what she wanted to do, above all else, was to clean him up and to get his body in proper alignment. While he cowered from her, she washed him off entirely and redressed his swollen ulcerated legs. She then put him in the bed, so that his legs were now elevated—the way the doctor had prescribed almost a month before. By noon all was well on Astor Three. For the first time Kermit Newall, diabetic and potential amputee, was in a clean bed, washed and properly medicated.

And throughout all of this he hardly attempted to speak. When he did once or twice, Karen murmured angrily and gave a few provisional whacks on the dusty hassock. Surprisingly, Kermit yielded to this mixture of tender loving care and drill-sergeant brutality. It wasn't the normal nurse-patient relationship, Karen mused as she stood back and admired her handiwork, but it was certainly effective!

When Kermit was finally tucked in and she had the whole room cleaned up, Karen walked over to the bed and smiled. Kermit glared up at her. "Now don't you feel better?" she asked.

He didn't answer, and Karen could tell he was having trouble staying awake. It was a good sign. For the first time she began to feel sorry for him. She slowly walked over to the corner and picked up the cane, which she had propped there. She knew there was some risk, but she handed it back to him.

"I'm sorry for my behavior, Mr. Newall," she said with the generosity of a victor. Instead of thanking her, Kermit suddenly brandished the cane, and Karen moved out of range. He glared at her, although he was having difficulty keeping his eyes open.

"Girly," he said finally, "you are finished at this hospital. And before I am through you won't be able to get a job in this whole city!" He seemed quite sure of himself. "Now, get out of this room until I ring for you."

Karen gladly followed his instructions and left the room. It was incredible what a charge she had gotten out of the whole incident! What a sense of energy it gave her to fight back. She went to the station, did her charting, and chatted amiably with Linda. Purposely she said nothing about what had happened.

At around twelve-thirty the patients' lunch cart came up. Karen took Mr. Newall's tray and walked into the room. What she saw made her feel good. Kermit Newall was fast asleep, snoring away, for the first time in weeks. She was tempted to back out of the room, but she knew he hadn't eaten anything all day except black coffee. And so she quietly walked in and set the tray down on the over-bed table. He awoke with a snort.

"Mr. Newall," she said gently, "I've brought your lunch. But first let me take your blood pressure and temperature."

He picked up his cane and fingered the handle, tracing a pattern in the ivory with his long fingernails. Karen went about her work. She uncovered the tray for him and moved the over-bed table where he could easily reach it. She dreaded the possibility that he would throw the turkey, gravy, sweet potato, and creamed spinach all over the floor and walls—she could just see it! Instead he merely said, "Get out," but without his earlier vehemence.

She left and sat in the break room, reading a magazine. At one-thirty Dr. Talbot, his psychiatrist, checked in at the station. She went right up 'and introduced herself.

"Bob finally took a day off, eh?" asked Dr. Talbot, a short pleasant man of about forty. "About time he had a break." He spoke without looking up from the chart. "How'd you find the morning with Mr. Newall?"

"Fine," she said slowly. "It was an uneventful morning. Thank goodness your notes explained the sleep disturbance. That made his general hostility easy to understand. Poor man," she added in a deeply sympathetic tone, "I do feel bad about his level of paranoia." Dr. Talbot looked up from the notes and she gave a little laugh. "He seemed to find me quite threatening and mean." Dr. Talbot smiled back, convinced of the absurdity of this charge.

"Mr. Newall," Karen said, as they entered the room, "here is your psychiatrist." Kermit was hungrily gnawing on a piece of bread. "I'm sure you'll want your privacy, and so I'll wait outside for you, okay?"

Kermit glared at her. "Get out."

As she turned to leave Karen gave the doctor a quiet little "see what I mean" smile. Kermit couldn't see it, however, nor did he understand the smile Dr. Talbot gave in return.

Karen grabbed her bag and hurried down to the cafeteria. As she hoped, she found Clare sitting alone by the window. "Hi," she said. "Sorry, I'm late."

"Oh, hello, Karen," said Clare. "What are you doing—oh, I forgot. You drew Kermit Newall for the day. Take good care of him for us."

Karen smiled. "Don't worry, I intend to. What are we going to do about Joan? I'm afraid she'll never talk to me again. She's so angry."

"She'll get over it," said Clare. "I just hope this program is going to work for her. She didn't exactly go in voluntarily."

"It has to work," said Karen with conviction. "Have you had any contact with her?"

"I called but they wouldn't let me talk to her," said Clare. "That's part of the treatment in the detox phase."

"She must be so frightened," said Karen, shuddering. "We have to go see her as soon as we can. That's assuming she'll see us," she added apprehensively.

"I think she'll understand, once she gets straightened out," said Clare.

"What's she doing for money?" asked Karen. "Do you think I should offer to help out?"

"Her ex, Bob Miller, is giving her a loan," said Clare. "Don't worry. He can afford it, but it must be so difficult for Joan," she continued. "Nobody likes charity." She hesitated. "I can appreciate that."

Karen sensed Clare needed to talk. "So what's going on with you? I've been so busy with Heather and Norton this last month, I feel out of touch."

"Bad news," said Clare. "Ken's still out of work. This time it looks like the company might not reopen."

"Oh no. I'm so sorry to hear that!" said Karen.

"We'll be okay. We've been through this before," she said stoically.

Karen suddenly felt inadequate to comfort her friend. "If there's anything I can do . . ." she said with feeling.

"Don't worry about it," said Clare. "He's got applications in at a lot of places, and some good prospects. Something's bound to come up. So what's happening with you?" said Clare, trying to change the subject. "Have you seen Ben Kendall lately?"

Karen felt guilty, because she hadn't told Clare of their involvement in the rank-and-file movement. "Mostly I see him professionally," said Karen. "He's very kind to Heather."

"What about the un-mostly part?" Clare asked, smiling.

Karen laughed. "The un-mostly part? Well, if anything interesting happens, I promise to let you know."

* * *

Dr. Talbot was finishing logging his notes when Karen returned from lunch. He put his hand on her shoulder, and she turned abruptly. "Can I speak to you for a moment?" he asked gravely.

"Certainly," she said. "Is there anything wrong?"

"I don't know what you did to our patient in there, but you're certainly one terrific nurse!"

"Why, thank you!" said Karen.

"That man hasn't had a bath in months. He hasn't had any real sleep in weeks. Of course, you were right. He does have some peculiar ideas about you. For instance, he claims you assaulted him with a cane or walking stick." He laughed gently. "This kind of paranoid ideation is just a phase he is going through. To a large degree it is caused by his insomnia. You may not believe this, but Kermit Newall is not a bad fellow. For instance, he's been very generous to our hospital."

"So I've heard," said Karen. "He's quite a philanthropist."

"How ever did you get him into the bed, though? Poor Bob Fold has been trying for weeks!"

"Well," she said slowly, "I know this sounds silly, but I think he was genuinely afraid of me—God only knows why—and that made him quite pliant. I found him very cooperative."

Dr. Talbot shook her hand warmly. "Keep up the good work!"

"Don't worry, Doctor," said Karen, "I intend to!"

Karen returned to the room just as Mrs. Newall arrived. She was a big-boned woman in her early fifties, with a square jaw and quite startling red hair. She paid Karen half an hour early and thanked her profusely. "Bob Fold is coming back tomorrow," Mrs. Newall said in her chirping voice.

She called Heather and Norton. They were fine and wished her a nice weekend. She was lonely. Remembering Clare's comment, she called Ben.

"I can't really talk now," he said. "But I'd love to get together. Could you meet me tomorrow morning at nine-thirty or so and we'll have breakfast?"

"Great," said Karen with honest enthusiasm. She took a hot bath, had dinner, put on her pajamas, and read the left-over Sunday magazine section. She then set the radio for half an hour of classical music but was asleep before it shut itself off.

She awoke to the sound of her phone ringing. Glancing at the clock, she saw it was 8 A.M..

"Karen? This is Bob Fold. Listen, what did you do to Mr. Newall yesterday?"

"Are you angry, or what?"

"Angry?" asked Bob. "Are you kidding? You deserve the Nobel Prize for Nursing. He's like a new person. And he's so damn clean I hardly recognized him. He slept last night for the first time since I've had him. He's like a new man. And would you believe, he even told me he was happy to see me this morning. Asked me about my trip. Also, the doctors were up and think they have a chance to save his leg after all. Whatever you did, you've got to teach me your secret."

"My secret? Ever hear of 'spare the rod and spoil the child'? I don't know, Bob, I'm not sure the ends justify the means."

"I am," he said, laughing. "How about coming back to trim Howard Hughes's fingernails?"

"I don't think even the great Newall fortune would be enough to get me to do that," she said, laughing. "He's all yours." She hung up the phone, got out of bed, remembering her breakfast date, hurried about the apartment getting ready to go.

Karen found Ben waiting in line at the cashier, off the main lobby.

"It's great to see you," he said. "Are you going to go back on the Asher case?" he asked.

"Of course," she said easily. "I really miss them both. I'm planning to go back on Monday. Why?"

"No reason," he said. "I went by to take the bloods yesterday and you weren't there. Norton seemed a little overtired, and I was thinking maybe it would be a good thing for both of them if you were there." His turn at the window had come, and he scrawled his name across the back of his paycheck. "Let's go eat!" he said.

"Okay, but I've got to hurry. They're coming to deliver a love seat this morning."

He laughed. "Sorry, I always find that word so old-fashioned and funny. Hey, Karen, let's get some pancakes, I haven't had them in years.

"So, how are you doing?" he asked cheerfully when they had settled into a booth. "I didn't see you at the last meeting," he said.

"I didn't even hear about it," Karen said. "I've been so busy with the Ashers. I don't come by the hospital except to bring you specimens."

"It was great," he said. "You heard the board postponed their meeting again?"

"Again?" said Karen. "They're incredible!"

"This time Mackey said he needed more time for his counter-report. Actually, they're helping the rank-and-file nurse movement grow by leaps and bounds. Everyone's really mad. We're planning a demonstration to coincide with the board meeting next month."

"I'm really out of it, Ben," she said apologetically. "I haven't heard anything about it."

"I'll have to remember to call you," he said enthusiastically. To Karen, he seemed to have become somewhat zealous in the cause. "We're going to have a big protest on March fourth, the day of the meeting. I'll put you on my list of people to call—except that every time I call you, Karen, you're working."

She laughed, a bit uncomfortably. "I told you, I've been very busy. I just finished an exhausting relief case—Kermit Newall—and that was supposed to be my vacation!"

"You really should take better care of yourself, Karen," Ben said seriously. "Do you mind if I speak personally?" he asked shyly. "I think you should socialize more, have more fun. It's not good to work all the time, to get so wrapped up in your patients."

"I see you've been talking to Clare," Karen said, embarrassed.

"Maybe I have," he said, smiling. "But it's true all the same."

"What do you suggest?" she asked.

"How about taking a vacation?" he asked suddenly. She said nothing, so he pressed forward. "I've been thinking of going to the Caribbean. Why don't you think about a holiday at the beach?"

"You mean with you?" she asked finally.

"Not necessarily," he laughed. "A winter vacation at the beach could be just the thing you need. Not that it wouldn't be nice to have your company." He smiled, awkwardly.

Karen thought it over. She liked Ben and found him attractive. She knew there was more implied in the offer, and the idea of getting involved frightened her. "Thanks for the suggestion," she said. "I'll think about it. It's just, with Heather and everything, I can't get away."

"Sure, I understand," he said, a bit crestfallen. "I'm pretty busy in the lab right now myself. But I'm definitely planning to go as soon as I can." They switched easily to a discussion of the rank-and-file meeting. "The board has definitely decided to vote on March fourth. Here, let me give you the latest leaflet." He handed her a double-sided sheet, which she put in her pocket. "We're building for a big demonstration outside. I think it's going to be a big success if the momentum keeps up."

"I'm definitely going to try and be there," said Karen.

"That's wonderful," said Ben. Their pancakes arrived and they ate silently for a while. "Well," said Ben, rising, "nose to the grindstone." He finished his coffee. They walked into the sunny winter day. "I hope I haven't offended you," said Ben.

"Don't be silly," she said, embarrassed that he had brought the subject up again.

He, too, seemed slightly uncomfortable. "By the way, what happened to Joan Fisher? I heard she was let go by Clare. Is that true?" The word had spread, in garbled form, throughout the hospital.

"Let go?" she asked, bewildered. "If you mean fired, she wasn't."

"I didn't mean to pry," said Ben quickly. "It's just that I thought you three were so close . . ."

"We were," said Karen softly.

In the isolation unit of the hospital Stephanie lay beneath a plastic tent.

Dr. Sheila Barnes stood to one side, talking to the Taylors. Clare, too, had joined them. She had made it a habit to stop by the isolation unit every day and had become good friends with Stephanie. While the Taylors spoke to the doctor, Clare sat with Stephanie. Before her illness, Clare had sometimes become impatient with Stephanie's whining; she now saw behind it a keen, if frustrated, creativity.

"This is all so frightening," said Mrs. Taylor. "All this equipment. Stephanie's terrified. Isn't there any way to get her onto a normal floor?"

Dr. Barnes was sympathetic but tough. "I'm afraid not. We have to be very careful about contamination."

"Doctor," said Mr. Taylor anxiously. "I understand this thing may be spread by mosquitoes. She went to camp last summer and there were lots of mosquitoes. Do you think—"

"Wait a minute!" said Dr. Barnes, holding up her hands. "First of all, I've told you, we don't know whether or not Stephanie has AIDS."

"But I thought the blood tests . . ."

"The blood tests were not inconsistent with AIDS, Mr. Taylor. But there are other possibilities. Secondly, I don't know where you got this thing about the mosquitoes, but it seems a bit farfetched. I wouldn't worry about the camp for the moment."

He seemed reassured. Meanwhile, Stephanie was not getting appreciably better.

"I used to like it here," she confessed to Clare.

"It's natural to enjoy attention," said Clare.

Stephanie nodded, a bit shamefaced. "There were always doctors and nurses around. Sometimes I'd wake up and there'd be a whole crowd of them—both women and men— standing watching me." She paused for breath. "I didn't know there were so many women doctors and men nurses," she said. "When I grow up, I think I might become a pediatrician like Dr. Barnes."

"That is a great idea," said Clare. "Many people have become doctors because they were sick as children."

"Not because they got sick. Because they got better!" said Stephanie sharply.

Clare laughed.

"Sometimes the doctors bore me. I know just what they're going to say. 'We don't know yet, we have to take more tests, just a little more blood.' With their boring old vampire jokes. I get sick of it. You know, I missed all the good Christmas movies. Dr. Kendall said they'd get me a VCR up here, but not while I'm in the tent."

"Are you still drawing pictures?"

Stephanie nodded. "My mother got me a whole box of West German pastels. They're beautiful. I'm going to draw a picture of how everyone's faces look from inside the tent."

Clare thought this was a remarkable child.

"Joan Fisher thought it was a great idea, too," said Stephanie.

"Joan?" asked Clare, puzzled. "When did she tell you that?"

"Uh-oh, she told me not to tell anyone she was here. She came to see me a few days ago," Stephanie said proudly. "But she told me to keep it quiet. I think I just blew it."

Clare kept smiling, but her voice was uneven. "I'm surprised. Joan was supposed to be away for the next month or so. Well, I'm glad she looked in on you. That was really nice of her."

The Alcoholics Anonymous program of St. Barnabas was located far uptown. Clare and Karen agreed to share a taxi after work to get there. The driver took a shortcut through the park and quickly got lost. Five dollars later he was still only within a stone's throw of the hospital.

Clare was snappy with him, and generally uptight about money. The driver explained, in broken English, that this was his first week on the job. "More likely his first week in the country," Clare said bitterly. "Let's take the bus back."

When they pulled up in front of the center they were both in an irritable and anxious mood. The center was in an old gray stone building. The man at the desk directed them to Joan's room, which was up four winding stairs. Joan was not in the room. They found her in a large attractive library, with built-in bookshelves and high ceilings.

Despite herself, Joan's face momentarily lit up when they walked in. "Look what the cat dragged in," she said, quickly becoming blasé.

"How are you doing, Joan?" Clare asked.

"Not bad," said noncommittally. "Could be worse."

"Hiya, Joan," said Karen.

Joan gave her an almost imperceptible nod. Karen was hurt by this but, strangely, felt upset with Clare. Why should she bear the brunt of Joan's anger? Why didn't Clare stick up for her and share the burden?

"Well, this is really nice," said Clare.

"I'm glad you two could see it in your hearts to visit me here," said Joan. "After all, you condemned me to this place."

"Joan, we didn't condemn you," said Karen heatedly. "This is very nice," she said, looking all around, "and you must admit it's doing you some good."

"Oh, spare me, Karen!" said Joan with self-assurance.

"You look good," Karen said mildly.

"Well, thanks," Joan said. "I will admit to one thing. I do feel better for the rest. I was working myself into a tizzy. That crazy Captain Kirk was driving me up the wall. That's the truth."

"You'll be happy to hear that he's finally been transferred," said Clare.

"About time," said Joan, but she didn't seem awfully surprised.

"And Stephanie Taylor's doing well, too," said Clare carefully.

"Nice little girl," said Joan. "I'm glad. Send her my best."

"I'll be sure to do that," said Clare. She smiled but wished that Joan had been honest about leaving the center to visit Stephanie.

"Do you have to stay here all the time?" asked Karen, trying to get into the conversation.

"First two weeks you're supposed to be incommunicado," Joan said lazily. "After that it's between you and your sponsor." In spite of her hostile attitude, Karen sensed Joan was not entirely unhappy here.

"Ken's still laid off," Clare suddenly volunteered. "He's hating his role as 'Mr. Mom.'"

"I'm sorry," said Joan coolly. "I hope he's doesn't turn to the bottle to solve his problems. But if he does, I'm sure you'll take good care of him too."

A strained silence filled the room. It was as if the whole history of these three friends had been erased and they had nothing in common.

"Well, take care of yourself, Joan," said Clare, turning to leave.

"Hey, thanks for coming, guys," Joan said with a momentary regret for her sarcasm.

Karen said, "Call me any time, Joan. You know I'm always home at night." It was a feeble attempt at reestablishing the humor that used to come so easily. They all felt a terrible loss.

# *ELEVEN*

## *March*

On the morning of March fourth Ben's music alarm went off at six o'clock. A melodic Beatles song was playing on the radio, but at that hour it sounded as raucous as a brass band. Ben opened his eyes. After a moment he slid out of bed.

His apartment was underfurnished and shivery cold. He put on the light and made his way along the wall of bookshelves, washed in a hurry, and slipped into warm street clothes.

Thank God, no rain! Ben thought, looking out the window. He could make out a hint of dawn to the east. He took the shopping cart that stood by the door, racking his brain to remember everything he had been assigned to do. At the last minute he grabbed his fur-lined gloves, since the metal cart could become searingly cold against his hands. He then loaded the cart with the heavy bundles stacked by the door. Taking one last look around, he locked the door behind him and wheeled the squeaky cart down the quiet hall, into the elevator, and then out into the street.

By six-thirty he was standing across from the nurses'

dormitory. It looked more like a resort hotel than part of a scientific center. He stood between two narrow tenements, feeling like a character in a thirties novel. He looked up at the darkened windows of the dorm, but there was no sign of life there.

Holding a leaflet toward the streetlight, he read:

# FELLOW NURSES!!

The nursing administration of Riverview Hospital has refused all our efforts to negotiate the issue of nurses' notes.

Meanwhile, patients' lives are endangered by their refusal to integrate the notes. Recently on Astor Five a doctor gave chemotherapy by the wrong route, endangering the life of the patient. The doctor hadn't read the nurses' notes.

Monster Morgan has mocked our concerns and denied that we represent nurses in any way.

The time for action is now! We rank-and-file nurses are determined to take the respect which Charlotte & Co. refuse to give us.

We are dressed as "doctors" in suits and lab coats. During lunch hours and on our breaks we will walk this informational picket line to let the public know the danger they are in.

Patients and families—we will do nothing to disrupt your care or that of your loved ones. Please add your voices to ours, show your support, by signing a petition. We are patient advocates.

Today's the day to finally stand up for your rights! March Forth on March Fourth!

—RANK-AND-FILE COMMITTEE

Ben smiled nervously. The leaflet was a little immature, he knew. He had written part of it. He stood wonderng how many nurses would turn out for the demonstration. He hoped it would be enough to sway the board.

On the tenth floor of the dormitory a light suddenly went on and a curtain was drawn back. A face briefly appeared. Ten minutes later two bundled-up nurses came through the doors of the dormitory building. It was Jill and Ellen with her little girl.

"You've got the leaflets, great," Jill said, giving Ben's hand a reassuring squeeze. Ellen's daughter, too big to carry, stood half asleep at her side.

"Hot off the mimeo," said Ben.

"It looks great," said Jill, laughing. She admired the leaflet. "Just wait till Charlotte sees what we've got in store for her."

Ellen laughed, but with no joy, only a grim determination. "I've been waiting months for this day," she said. "I'd give anything to see Charlotte's face when she sees our picket line. Take a picture, Ben," she said. He laughed uneasily. Ellen had become more bitter as the day of confrontation approached. "It's a great thing you're doing, Ben," she added. "Without your help 'Rank-and-File Nurses' could have become very unbalanced."

Ben gave a boyish smile. He didn't contradict her, because what she said was true. "I'd love to join you on the picket line," he said.

"You'd better not," Jill said, punching his shoulder. They had developed a strong bond of camaraderie by working for this common cause.

"You stick to the collective decision, Doctor," Ellen added with mock toughness. "Your place is in the board-room. Please keep out of sight at the demonstration. If you blow your cover we'll lose your vote today!"

Ben nodded. He really didn't want to jeopardize his position at the hospital. "Well, it's a quarter to eight," said

Ben, checking his watch. "If none of the others show by eight, I guess you'll have to start without them."

"They'll show," said Ellen. Her daughter hugged her leg and mumbled.

Just then they spotted several figures hurrying along on the other side of the stree. There were three women, talking animatedly. They had large doctors' lab coats over their jackets.

"Here come some of them," said Jill excitedly. "I hope they know how to behave on the picket line." The young nurses approached.

"Up early this morning, aren't you?" Ellen joked easily.

"Hold the fort, for we-e-e are coming!'" one of them sang. They all laughed. Together, this small knot of people made their way toward the hospital. Outside the Greek diner they met up with five other group members, including a housekeeper whom Jill had privately nicknamed "the human bullhorn."

Ben nodded to Ellen and went into the diner. He ordered coffee and an almond danish and settled into one of the booths near the window. From this ringside seat he could watch the action directly across the street.

"Hey, get your leaflets here," cried the human bullhorn in her friendly barker's voice. "What are you afraid of, think it's gonna bite?" she yelled at the back of a retreating psychiatrist. He laughed but didn't stop.

Ben could hear her through the plate glass and knew exactly what was happening. Ellen moved with self-assurance she had gained by being involved with this group. He watched her assigning a crew to cover the various entrances to the hospital, handing out leaflets, dealing with emergencies like a football coach. Secretly, he wished Karen would arrive early. Finally Ben couldn't stand it anymore. He paid his bill and went outside, to stand on the periphery of the demonstration. He wasn't going to watch from the window, even if it meant being seen.

"Well, here we are!" said a nurse he recognized from the Astor Pavilion. She was not a regular member of the group, in fact he had heard her criticize the leaflets. Yet here she was, dressed in a white lab coat, carrying a homemade sign that read, INTEGRATE NURSES' NOTES NOW! It was a good omen. With her were about ten or a dozen other nurses and nurses' aides, many of them from the same floor. If this kept up, half the hospital would be involved by the midmorning break.

At eight o'clock Ben went to a pay phone in the rear of the diner.

"Yeah?" said a sleepy voice on the other end.

"Harrison Chambers, please," said Ben. Just saying the name gave him a bit of a tingle. Chambers was the dean of city news reporters. Ben and Jill had met with him at the studio a few nights before, to inform him about the impending action. He had given them his home phone number and was now their friend.

"You got him," said the street-wise voice.

"Hi, Mr. Chambers," said Ben. "This is Dr. Ben Kendall. Do you remember we met the other night?"

"Why, of course, Ben," said Chambers, recovering from a momentary loss of memory. "What can I do for you so early in the morning?"

"You asked me to inform you if the protest came off," said Ben shyly. "It's happening right now. About fifty nurses have joined the picket line already and there are move coming all the time," he said, exaggerating a bit. "If I were you, I'd come down right away. Just ask for Ellen. She's leading the action."

"That's great, Doctor," said Chambers. "I'll definitely pass the word along. Thanks so much for calling."

Ben's heart sank. He had promised the group he could deliver Chambers for the demonstration. He hesitated, then plunged in. "You know, there might be some violence. The guards have been pushing the nurses back. I'd appreciate it if you'd come right over here."

"What do you mean by pushing?" asked Chambers, suddenly interested.

"The hospital guards are carrying nightsticks. Rumor has it that the administration's going to call the police. The atmosphere is very tense," he added, improvising. "I think there very well might be a clash." He almost had himself convinced by the time he hung up.

The diner owner overheard and looked at him as if he were crazy. There was absolutely nothing violent happening across the street. If this worked well, he thought, maybe he should also call the news desks of the dailies or even the networks!

It was only about half an hour later that a cream-colored van pulled up and a snappily dressed Harrison Chambers hopped out, microphone in hand. There were no security guards in sight, but by now it didn't matter. The demonstration had become news.

The number of nurses had grown after the eight o'clock shift change; almost all of them had on lab coats. Nurses leaving the hospital were attracted to the growing picket line and to the commotion caused by Chambers' arrival.

Karen came over before going to the Ashers'. She carried a picket sign for about half an hour. Ben looked at her from across the crowd and waved. She waved back but continued to march. Just as she was leaving she spotted Joan and rushed over to greet her. "I didn't expect to see you here!"

said Karen. "I thought you were against integrating the notes."

Joan seemed unsure whether to speak to Karen at all. "Did I say that?" she asked cooly. "I've changed my mind. Did you expect me to check with you and Clare?" she added sarcastically.

"I'm glad you changed your mind," said Karen, keeping a friendly tone.

"Surprised they let me out of the zoo?" Joan asked provocatively. She saw someone she knew and turned to a friendly conversation, leaving Karen standing alone.

Chambers was wandering among the crowd with his cameraman. "What exactly do you hope to accomplish by this job action?" he asked, brandishing the mike. The minicam focused on Ellen.

"We hope to demonstrate to the administration that we nurses consider the issue of integrated progress notes a life-and-death matter."

"Why are nurses' notes so important?" asked Chambers. "Aren't you just quibbling over words?"

"Not at all," said Ellen forcefully, and several nurses shouted their agreement. "As it stands, the nurses' notes are ignored by some medical staff. This can lead to nursing observations being overlooked. We want to change that. We want to get the respect that professional nurses deserve."

"Doesn't this sort of action endanger patients?" he asked. To Ben, it sounded as if he had been talking to Charlotte Morgan.

"Not at all," said Ellen calmly. "We've purposely chosen this sort of action because it does not harm patients in any way. Ultimately," she added, "we are fighting for better care for the patients. That's what it's all about, really."

"What do the other nurses think?" Chambers turned to

the human bullhorn. "Well, yes, I agree," she stammered. Unlike Ellen—who relished the publicity—the bullhorn suddenly became shy and reserved. "Of course, you see, I'm not a nurse actually . . ."

Chambers feigned surprise. "You're not a nurse?" He read out loud the sign the aide was wearing around her neck: RIVERVIEW NURSES DEMAND BETTER TREATMENT.

"Do you at least work at the hospital?"

"She's an aide, a *nurse's* aide," said Jill, her color rising.

"Oh, I thought you were one of those 'outside agitators' the administration has told us about," said Chambers, laughing slyly.

"Absolutely not," Ellen said, now thrown on the defensive. "We have all sorts of people in our group. We have nurses, nurses' aides, some secretaries, even some doctors." Chambers smiled knowingly. "We've even got some patients in our group. Riverview nurses are the majority."

Karen joined in the applause for this speech; but there were also some boos. The crowd was growing in size every minute, as the office workers appeared.

"Do you seriously think that this sort of thing can influence the board's decision, or intimidate them?" he asked.

"We don't know. We hope the vote goes our way." Ellen said. "And if this doesn't work," she added with self-assurance, "we'll have to consider other measures!"

"We will not be intimidated!" Dr. Mackey was red in the face, and the meeting had only just begun.

"Dr. Mackey," said Clare levelly, "I don't think the aim of this demonstration is to intimidate anybody."

"Have you been outside lately? There's an angry horde of people out there, screaming their heads off. And what really peeves me is that they've taken to the airwaves to voice their grievances."

"Washing our dirty linen in public," said Dr. Stover sadly. "It's so unprofessional."

"Well, I heard the radio report, and it didn't seem outrageous to me," said Clare. "In fact it seemed to make a lot of sense." She took a sip of the orange juice that had been provided, along with the cold cuts, for the lunchtime meeting.

"Did you know that Ellen was a subversive when you hired her?" Mackey shot back. "And Jill what's-her-name? My department is making a list."

Ben grimaced. Subversive! If it hadn't been for Mackey, Ellen would probably still be working at the hospital.

"What do you mean, 'subversive'?" Ben asked. He had to watch himself. His voice was beginning to show emotion.

"She's the leader of that mob outside, isn't she?" Mackey demanded. "These people are well organized, well oiled, well financed."

Ben had to smile. All the money for the leaflets had come from their own pockets. "Come off it, Mackey," Ben said, smiling broadly. "How much money do you think it takes to put out a leaflet?"

"You tell me," said Mackey smartly.

Dr. Greenberg whispered, to no one in particular, "Ho boy! This is gonna be some meeting!"

Ben tried not to show any reaction to this. Mackey was just taking potshots—or was he?

"I tell you," Mackey continued, "they're trying to undermine the doctor's authority in the hospital. There's always a pecking order. Someone's got to lead, whether you call him a boss, supervisor, or Pope. That's human nature."

"I hardly think this is relevant to our problem," said Clare.

Even Dr. Stover, the hospital director, was beginning to squirm. "Your point, Dr. Mackey?"

"My point is this!" Mackey licked his thumb and quickly started shuffling through a stack of papers. "And this! And this!" He pulled out copies of the morning's leaflet and scattered them helter-skelter on the well-polished table. "This is a call to revolution at Riverview." He passed out leaflets to everyone around the table. "So wake up and smell the coffee! Take a good look at what's going on outside. Nurses playing doctor. Next thing, they'll want to write prescriptions. Give orders. Perform surgery. Why not? They do everything else!" There were chuckles at this. Even Ben had to admit Mackey was amusing in his way.

"I fear this meeting is becoming a brouhaha," said Dr. Stover, with his Boston accent.

"I think Dr. Mackey is making an important point," said Charlotte. She was especially well turned out, with a silk blouse and blue suit. "We can't succumb to the rule of the mob," she said. "As a nurse, of course, I am for upgrading the status of my profession. but to make any changes at this point would only confirm the fact that we are weak. We can't allow ourselves to be influenced by this group."

Ben had been listening to all this with growing frustration. "This is so childish," he said impatiently. "All you can think about is how we *look*." He spoke earnestly, affecting almost everyone with his honesty. Even Dr. Mackey was caught up. "Theoretically"—he dragged the word out—"we are all healers. Our mission is to help the patients get well."

Mackey had recovered from his momentary lapse. "What's that got to do with a bunch of loonies running loose in our corridors?"

Ben proceeded as if he hadn't heard this. "There are a number of issues involved here," he said. The words came out with authority—a new experience for him. "There is the technical one of how we organize our notes. *Our* notes. We healers, which includes all of us, doctors, nurses, and support workers. Dr. Mackey has brought us some data"—he held up a neatly foldered report—"and Ms. Henson has brought us the other side. I have worked in hospitals where the notes are integrated. It works very well."

Mackey grimaced until his lips virtually disappeared. "Are you contradicting me?" he demanded.

Ben smiled but kept going. "More important, however, is the question of our morale. There is an indefinable spirit to a hospital—" Mackey guffawed, and the serious mood was in danger of breaking up. "Yes, Dr. Mackey, there is a spirit—either of cooperation and good will among the staff or of hostility and competition. Everybody loses when the staff is unhappy, when the nurses are overworked, when there is high absenteeism and high turnover."

Charlotte Morgan turned to Dr. Mackey and addressed him directly. "Dr. Kendall certainly makes a lot of sense," she said.

"Don't be ridiculous!" Mackey said scornfully. "The nurses around here get everything they want. Just look out the window, you'll see your nurses, Charlotte. Not worth much, if you ask me!" Mackey was practically screaming.

"Is that right?" asked Ben, seeing his chance to bait him into saying something else. "Don't you think the nurses are underpaid for what they do?"

"Underpaid? For hanging around drinking coffee in the lounge from morning to night? Dragging out their chores, so they can pick up back-to-back shifts, double and triple time? They could all be replaced by Japanese robots and the world wouldn't be the wiser!"

"Now just a minute!" said Charlotte Morgan. For a small woman, she had a remarkably authoritative air when she got riled. "I have sat here and listened to this provocation long enough, Dr. Mackey. I sympathized with your point of view, but I am also impressed with the sentiments I heard expressed this morning on the picket line."

"My point of view?" he asked, truly surprised. "Wasn't this your pont of view last week?"

"I'm beginning to have second thoughts about this whole matter," she said testily.

Clare saw her opportunity. "This was never meant to be a confrontation between the nurses and doctors. What we are after is better conditions for everyone. The doctors will profit by having easier access to the nurses' comments, and vice versa."

"You know, Phil," said Dr. Cordell, a young orthopedist with a head of curly hair, "we've got to thank our lucky stars that all these nurses have done is set up an informational picket line. I was at Barnabas when the big strike took place. You wouldn't have liked that, Phil! I think the nurses have behaved quite admirably through all of this. Dignified and restrained. I'm very impressed."

"I sense a gargantuan cave-in in progress," said Mackey bitterly. "Rolling over every time a bunch of hysterical women create a scene is not the answer. You've got to stand up to them, let them know who's boss."

Ben, of course, had a rebuttal for this, but he was glad to see others taking up his role.

"These are hysterical women?" said Cordell, embarrassed. "Seemed pretty peaceful to me."

"I was shoved on my way into the hospital this morning!" Mackey rebutted.

"I saw what happened, Phil," said Dr. Stover. Everyone turned to listen. Stover rarely voiced his own opinion until

the end of a discussion. "You took one of these leaflets"—
he lifted one up from the conference table and let it fall from
his hand—"and then you ripped it up and threw it at a
nurse." Stover smiled his sweet, slightly abstracted smile.

"What if I did?" Mackey asked defiantly. "We're
fighting for the future of this institution. Do you want us to
go the way of the city hospitals, where discipline is
nonexistent? Why don't you tell how they surrounded me?"

"Didn't you tell a nurse the board was going to get an
injunction?"

"I don't remember that," said Mackey, as if on the
witness stand. "What if I did? I was talking to one of the
instigators. Jill Curtis. I want her fired right away."

"Jill?" said Charlotte, surprised. "She's one of our best
nurses. Is Jill involved in this?" She turned to Clare.

"I don't know," said Clare. "It seems to me a lot of good
nurses are involved."

"I suggest we put this matter to a vote," said Ben,
seizing the moment.

"What about my report? Has anybody read it?" asked
Mackey a bit desperately.

"I certainly did," said Dr. Stover. "Frankly, you've
simply rehashed the same arguments we've all heard
before, and are still hearing today."

"I don't need to read it, Phil," said Dr. Greenberg. "Too
busy. Don't even have time to read my daughter's report
card."

Dr. Sage, the acting head of neurology, pointed one
finger in the air until he was called on. "I think we should
postpone any vote," he said. "Emotions are running too
high for us to be objective. Besides, maybe this whole thing
will blow over."

"We've already postponed it three or four times! If we
postpone the vote any more," said Clare heatedly, "that

will be a signal to the people outside, as well as those inside, that we hold them in comtempt. We'll look like vacillating fools if we refuse to vote now."

"Well, I for one agree," said Dr. Stover. "I suggest that we finally have a vote here and now."

"Yeah, let's get this over with," said Dr. Greenberg. "I've got important things to tend to. Like lunch."

"I call for a secret ballot, then," said Mackey. "So everyone can vote his conscience without fear of intimidation."

There was muted laughter at this. "We've never had secret ballots before," said Stover. "Why start now?" Ignoring Mackey's protests, he said, "All those in favor of integrating the nurses' and the doctors' notes, please raise your hands."

Ben and Clare were first with their hands up. To their surprise, they were followed by Charlotte Morgan, who had clearly had a profound change of heart. Charlotte's conversion had had a dramatic effect. Several other board members also raised their hands. That brought to six the number in favor of Clare's proposal.

"Those against?" asked Dr. Stover.

Mackey, of course, raised his hand high. "Why don't you raise 'em both?" Dr. Greenberg quipped, but he joined Dr. Mackey in voting no. So too, in the end, did Dr. Sage and a number of other doctors. There were six against.

"It's a tie," said Greenberg. "Good, let's get back to work."

"Wait a minute," said Ben. "Dr. Stover didn't vote."

Stover nodded his large, pale head and pushed out his lips. "I guess I didn't," he said. "Well, in that case, I guess I'm the tie breaker." He was enjoying the suspense.

"I for one would have no objection to letting you decide this issue, Dr. Stover," said Mackey with an ingratiating smile. "I know we can trust you to arrive at the right decision."

"I'm glad you think so," said Stover. "I'm not in favor of equality between nurses and doctors, you understand." He paused. "But I do think that what the nurses have to say is usually important for the doctors to know. This small issue is symbolic of the direction medical care must take. Therefore," he sighed, "I've decided to vote in favor of Ms. Henson's proposal."

"Okay!" Ben said, bringing his hand down loudly on the conference table. Clare looked astounded, then beamed at him.

Stover paused, looking straight at Phil Mackey. "And now, if there's no further business, the meeting is adjourned!"

Outside in the hallway, Ben grabbed Clare's hand in both of his and shook it warmly. "They're going to go crazy when they hear this outside," said Ben.

"Let's hope not. I really just want to get them back to work as soon as possible." She hesitated. "I know Jill and Ellen very well. They told me they've had a lot of support from other disciplines." Clare was smiling openly.

Ben said nothing, his color rising. "What are you getting at?" he asked cautiously.

"Nothing. It's just that the nurses' aides, housekeepers, and even some of the patients have been very suportive." She continued to smile.

He paused for a moment, put some money in a drink machine, and got out a grapefruit juice. "Wow, cold," he said, trying to change the subject.

"Do you think any doctors joined the rank and file?"

Ben smiled. Clare got on the elevator and turned back. "Good work, Ben," she said quietly. The doors closed.

\* \* \*

Although it was still March, it was a magnificent spring morning. Karen had risen early, feeling relaxed and refreshed. As she walked to work she opened her jacket and let her arms swing unself-consciously.

Despite the constant spread of Heather's disease, her pain was well controlled. Karen would have her breakfast with Heather as usual. She always enjoyed their mornings together.

As soon as she turned the key in the door she knew somthing was wrong. Terribly wrong. There was a disturbing odor in the vestibule. When she hung her coat on the Victorian hatrack she could hear a noise coming from the sitting room off the entrance hallway. Opening the large door, she found the source of the noise: Norton was lying sprawled on the velvet couch, his head back against the bolster. The stereo was on, a blues record Norton and Heather used to play when they were in a melancholy mood. At the side of the sofa was a nearly empty bottle of scotch. Karen surmised from the look of things that Norton had drunk most of it.

He had been crying. His swollen face was puffy and red. He glanced at Karen pathetically and began to cry into a pillow. "I guess I'm not a drinking man," he said, blubbering into the pillow.

"Norton. What's going on?" She felt panicky.

"She's upstairs," said Norton. "I'll stay here." He rolled over on his side.

"What happened, Norton?" she asked. Her pulse was racing. "Tell me."

"Upstairs," said Norton. "I just want to rest now."

Karen couldn't wait for the tiny elevator. She raced up the circular staircase. She realized now that the smell was not just Norton's booze but human waste.

She rushed into the room and found Heather lying on the

floor. She was wedged between the bed and the floral print armchair she used for afternoon reading. Her wet nightgown clung to her. She lay perfectly still. After a moment of horror Karen took her pulse. It was slow and regular—borderline normal—about fifty beats per minute. Her breath, like her pulse, was also slow and regular. Karen pulled off her dirty bedclothes and washed her body with warm soapy water. She lifted Heather easily onto the bed. Her body was pathetically small and emaciated. She stirred and seemed to mumble something. Karen put clean clothes on her, arranged her in a comfortable position, and went back downstairs.

"Listen, Norton, I need your utmost cooperation now!" she said sternly.

"I'll be okay now," said Norton. "What a night! The worst night of my life."

"All right, I'll put some water on for coffee. You go in there and wash up. Then you tell me exactly what happened."

He returned a few minutes later with half his face shaved, a bloody nick on his chin. "I swear to God," he said, groaning as he sat down, "I was not meant to drink. Sorry."

"Tell me what happened," said Karen, handing him a cup of black coffee.

"Will she . . . I mean, is she . . . going to live?" he said, his eyes tearing again.

"Yes, Norton, she's fine," said Karen. "You can relax."

"Oh, God! I can't believe it," he said, amazed. "I saw her. It was terrible. She tried to get up out of her bed, but she fell. I couldn't stand it. It's horrible. If I had known . . ."

"Norton, why did you think she was dead?" Karen asked; she was beginning to suspect why.

"Because I gave her an overdose!"

"You what?" said Karen.

"Of course. Didn't you know? I thought for sure you understood what was going on," he said, shaking his head.

"I want to know what exactly went on here last night," Karen said, her color rising. "Your wife is not dead, nor is she dying. Her pulse and respiration are normal."

"Oh, my God," said Norton, and he seemed truly grieved. "What a failure I am."

"Look, Norton," Karen said impatiently, "I have to know how much medicine you gave her."

"It's simple. I gave her a whole bottle of the pain medicine. I thought that would be enough to put her to sleep." Norton stared at Karen across the room. "So now you know. Are you going to turn me in to the police?"

Despite his apparent coherence, he was still a little drunk. Karen stared at him and thought for a moment. "Look, Norton, whatever you *think* you did, you certainly didn't kill your wife or harm her in any way as far as I can see. Heather even said thank you to me when I got her cleaned up and in bed. I want you to promise me that nothing like this will happen again. If I can't have your word, I'm signing off the case."

"Karen," he said, staring at her with his reddened eyes, "I can't go on like this. I need you. I don't know what I would do if you walked off."

"Norton," she said, shaking her head with pity. He suddenly seemed like such an old man—not the youthful and vibrant Norton she had met a few months before. "Norton, just promise me that you'll never do anything like this again."

"It was her request, Karen," he said firmly.

"She asked you to do it? I find that very hard to believe. I can't imagine Heather doing such a thing."

He paused. "We discussed it many times, how it would

be better to die in your sleep than to suffer the endless agony of terminal cancer. Before we knew she had cancer we discussed it, and we always agreed . . . a living will . . ." His voice trailed off. "Oh, Christ, I can't believe I messed this up! If only I had given her a bigger dose it would be all over now. All the suffering and the pain."

Karen listened but was impatient to interrupt. "First of all," she said, "I don't know what Heather may have said when she was well, but every day I see her fighting for her life."

Norton sat with compressed lips but said nothing.

"Furthermore," she added, "the medication is kept right by her bedside. Any time she wanted to she could have taken it herself, if that's what she wanted."

"And done a better job at it than me," Norton said.

"But she didn't do it. She didn't want to die. You're laboring under a misconception, Norton. Dying people almost never want to commit suicide. It's as simple as that. I've seen it dozens of times. People make all kinds of elaborate plans to kill themselves when they're not there yet. What happens? The closer the end approaches, the more they cling to life!"

"You don't understand. She said—"

"I don't care what she said once upon a time, Norton," Karen said gently. "You attempted murder."

They sat in silence, Norton with his eyes averted. He sighed and put his head in his hands. "Well, thanks for the coffee," he said finally.

She didn't answer him.

"I know you care about her, but no one could love her as much as I do," he said. "She's going to die soon, don't you see that? Nothing you or anyone does is going to save her." He was trying to be rational, but choked up.

"She's not suffering," Karen said softly, with assurance.

"Her physical pain has been managed very well with the morphine solution. And her mental attitude is superb. She's handling everything beautifully." He moaned at this, covering his face with his hands.

"The mental anguish. You don't know, Karen. . . . She's not herself when you're here. It comes out when you leave. She's just . . . *entertaining* you, like a favorite daughter."

These words were like a harsh blow across the face. "No, I don't believe that! I'm sure she has mental anguish," said Karen coolly, "but it's balanced by her incredible appetite for new ideas, thoughts, and experiences."

"Come on, Karen. It's just the drugs," he said bitterly. "She's just high all the time now."

"There's something else, too. Her personality. She just has a good outlook."

"You think so?" He looked up.

"Now let's not talk about Heather, Norton," she said, taking a deep breath, "let's talk about you. I think you're overtired, and I want to get nurses around the clock to help you with Heather."

Norton cut her off with a self-deprecating gesture. "Forget about me!"

"I'm only here for one shift. It would be better for Heather to have two people in the house. Come on, Norton. Let me arrange nurses around the clock."

"Three nurses full time?" He sounded dubious.

"Why not?" she asked.

"I just hate to create so much trouble."

"I'll make all the arrangements. First I'd better check on Heather, though." Karen went up to Heather's bedroom and checked her vital signs again. The pulse and heartbeat had risen slightly. She seemed comfortable. Thinking over her plan, Karen realized she would have a difficult time finding two private nurses she could trust.

Karen came back to the living room. Norton gave her a bear hug. Karen held him close for a minute and could feel the tension in his body. "Listen, Norton, why don't you go for a walk? You can get me a dozen eggs and I'll make you an egg salad." It was Heather's favorite dish. She called it her "cholesterol special."

"Okay, I'll go out. I'll try to find those good brown eggs you told me about."

"In the meantime, I'll arrange for the extra nurses."

Karen looked in on Heather and then went into the library. She knew what she had to do.

Karen sat on the edge of Heather's ottoman in the libary and called Joan. In the past month Karen had reconciled herself to Joan's anger.

"Hi, Joan," said Karen, trying to be cheerful. "How are you doing?"

"Hello, Karen!" Joan said with surprise. "To what do I owe the honor?" Karen was glad to hear that Joan wasn't entirely unfriendly. "I hope you're not calling to lecture me. It would be nice to talk to someone about something other than the perils of ethanol."

Karen laughed. "Did you stay for the outcome of the vote?" she asked.

"No, but I heard about it on TV," said Joan. 'Score one for Clare."

"So," Karen said, after a pause, "when are you going back to work?"

"As soon as Clare thinks I'm sufficiently dehydrated," she quipped.

"How's it really going, Joan?" Karen asked, trying to break through the sarcasm.

"You're referring to my financial state, of course?"

"Yes," said Karen.

"Bob Miller is being disgustingly generous. He's really enjoying his role as my savior. You know, I'm really still very angry at both you and Clare. That's something I just have to work out. I don't think I want to talk to you about my personal life." It was clear from the final tone in Joan's voice that she had been waiting for an opportunity to deliver this speech.

"I'm sorry you feel that way," said Karen, deflated. "I was calling to ask a favor."

Joan hesitated. "Oh, really? What sort of favor?"

"Heather Asher," Karen said.

"What about her?" asked Joan in a more professional tone of voice. "Don't tell me . . ."

"No, she's still alive," said Karen. "But barely. You know, her cancer's metastasized."

"Oh, Christ," Joan said softly. "Are they keeping her pain under control?"

"Yes. She has liquid pain medication when she's awake, and we inject morphine into her heart via the Broviac when she's asleep."

"I'm sorry, Kar.' I know how involved you are in this case. so I can imagine how upset you are. Where are you?"

"Actually, Joan, I'm calling from the Ashers' house. What I was hoping was that you might come to work with Heather."

There was a long silence. "You mean as a private nurse? What about you?"

"Look, Joan, I desperately need two other nurses I can trust," Karen said. "I don't want to discuss it on the phone, but I can say it's quite urgent. Believe me, I wouldn't ask you unless it was really important."

"Well, I don't know, Kar'. What about the hospital? Couldn't they supply you with some names?" Joan asked.

"I can't have strangers, Joan. I need someone who can keep a secret," said Karen.

"Thanks for the vote of confidence. But I don't know. I've never done a home case." She hesitated. "What hours did you have in mind?"

"You regular shift, four to twelve," Karen said, holding her breath.

"Well . . ." She was silent, debating inside her head. "Okay. I guess I'm scared in a way. I'll have to speak to my sponsor about it."

"You would have made a good Moonie," Karen said, laughing.

Joan laughed freely and spontaneously for the first time in the conversation. "You think AA is a cult? Well, just to show you, I'm gonna do it! As long as my guru agrees, that is."

"I can't thank you enough," said Karen, exhaling her breath. She hung up and dialed the hospital.

Karen heard Heather moan. She went into her room and knelt at the bedside, giving her a gentle shake. "Heather?" she asked.

Heather opened her eyes and blinked at the light. "Oh, my God, it's daytime already. You know how I *hate* to sleep in the daytime." She yawned and struggled to keep her eyes open. "It makes me feel like a lazy bum. I'm so tired. I dreamed I was buying hats in Haiti. One after another after another. Like Dr. Seuss. What time is it, dear?"

"Two o'clock," said Karen. "Time for your medicine." Actually, Karen was anxious to see how she'd feel when she awoke, since she had missed several doses.

Norton had returned and was standing in the doorway. "How is she, Karen?" he whispered.

"Norton?" Heather asked, peering. Even in the best of times she hadn't seen too well without her glasses. "Why did you let me sleep so long?" she chided. "You know how I hate to sleep the day away." She smiled and raised her eyebrows, mocking her illness.

"Are you feeling all right?" Norton asked uncertainly.

"I feel okay," she said drowsily. Her voice trailed off. She was in pain.

Karen poured the thick morphine solution into a glass and gave it to Heather. In a few minutes, when she was sound asleep again, Karen and Norton crept out of the room. The beautiful weather had changed. A cool breeze was coming through the window, billowing out the lacy curtains. In the distance she could hear the rumble of thunder.

"Did you get two nurses?" Norton asked nervously as he moved to close the windows. "You know, it's really not necessary," he added in a low voice. "I'm not going to do anything now."

"I got my friend Joan Fisher from the SICU to agree to come in for one shift. I was just getting ready to call about the night shift."

"Karen," he said, "I'm happy she's alive. I'm going to enjoy her wonderful spirit, her wonderful *mind*, which has been God's gift to me since we were just kids together." He pressed his lips together, unable to continue.

"I understand," said Karen.

"I believe you do. You know, Heather thinks of you as a daughter, Karen. The daughter she always wanted."

"Thank you, Norton. My mother died when I was little. In my own way, I think of Heather as the perfect mother." She realized the truth of it as she spoke the words, one by one.

* * *

"I've been meaning to call you," said Clare enthusiastically. "I wanted to tell you all about the vote." She and Karen were sitting at the counter of Pistachio Park, an ice cream parlor a few blocks from the hospital.

"Of course, I saw it on TV. What's the inside story?" asked Karen. Her sundae came and she took a spoonful. "I saw Dr. Mackey. He looked livid."

Clare laughed. "He was fit to be tied. Actually, he made such a fool out of himself Charlotte came over to our side."

"You are kidding!" Karen exclaimed.

"She may live to regret it," said Clare softly. "Mackey has called for her resignation. I don't think anything will come of it."

"Look, Clare," said Karen, "we could spend the whole afternoon discussing Riverview politics, but I bought you that ice cream as a bribe. I need a favor."

Clare raised her eyebrows.

"It's Heather Asher. Do you think you could moonlight on the twelve-to-eight shift?"

"Karen, just because Ken has been laid off, I don't need any handouts."

"Clare, you completely misunderstand," said Karen. She lowered her voice. "I'm only telling you this in complete confidence. Norton Asher tired to overdose his wife this morning before I got to work."

"Oh, my God!" Clare exclaimed.

"I need nurses around the clock. Joan is working four to twelve right now. I just don't think I can handle sixteen hours every day. Will you do it?"

"This is such a shock," said Clare. "Joan? Do you think that's wise?"

"Yes," said Karen with more conviction than she felt.

"She has to start working sometime. I needed her and she agreed."

"Look, you know I could use the money, but I can't handle two back-to-back shifts. Maybe I could do it for a week or two now that Ken's home with the kids. I guess I could take some vacation days from Riverview," she thought out loud. "Naturally, I'd have to talk it over with Ken."

"Clare, I don't want to beg," said Karen. "But could you call Ken right now and discuss this with him? It would be best if you could start tonight."

"Okay, Karen," said Clare, standing up. "But no guarantees."

It was just a week later, at shift change, that Heather's condition took a dramatic turn for the worse.

Clare was working the midnight shift, and Karen had arrived early at the apartment to have her breakfast. Norton was in the upstairs kitchen brewing coffee. Karen was reading over the notes that the three of them kept on a clipboard on the desk outside Heather's room.

Clare came out. "Oh, hi, Kar', you're early."

"What's the matter?" Karen asked. She sensed a change in Clare's mood.

"It's pretty bad," said Clare. "It won't be long now. Joan said she noticed Heather's heartbeat was becoming markedly more irregular. She lost bowel control during the night," said Clare, evading Karen's eyes. "I'm sure you've seen that toward the end." Her voice was calm.

"It might be something else." Karen thought for a minute. "It might be the vitamin C."

Clare smiled. "Maybe. I don't want to upset her by suggesting she stop, though. You know how she clings to those vitamins."

Norton had approached, in his robe and slippers, with a tray ful of coffee and rolls. He had caught the word "upset," and that frightened him. "Who's upset? Something upset Heather?" he asked nervously.

Clare spoke in a flat, even voice. "Karen was wondering if the vitamin C could have upset her stomach."

"Could it?" he asked promptly.

"Maybe, maybe not," said Karen.

"Well, who knows?" he said, dismissing it. "When we first sailed up the Golfo de California she got a case of Montezuma's Revenge you wouldn't believe. We had to stop in at La Paz for medicine. But she got better then!"

"Poor Heather," said Karen. Clare stared at her: she spoke those words with such deep feeling that it was obvious she was thinking of Heather as she was today.

"That didn't stop her, not one bit," said Norton. "In fact, a day later, she wanted to take off inland. We rented a dune buggy down there, and off we went, against my better judgment. In case you haven't noticed she has me wrapped around her little finger." They all laughed. "If you're not careful, I'll be breaking out the slide projector! Here's your coffee."

Karen took her coffee mug, a gift from Heather which had the word "NURSE" on it, but Clare shook her head. "I'm going home to go to sleep." She picked up the clipboard and started to make her entries.

"Well, send Ken my best," said Karen, smiling. "I guess today the two of you will have the run of the house, with the kids off at school."

"No, Ken's got a really important job interview today," said Clare with pride. Just then they heard a muffled sound from Heather's room. "She was sleeping just a minute ago," said Clare. "I'll go in."

"Don't be ridiculous. You go home. I want to say good

morning to her anyway." Karen went in and and quietly closed the door behind her. Heather's kerchief had fallen away, revealing an almost completely bald head. Could this be the same person who went trekking in the deserts of Baja? She was not even the same woman Karen had met at Riverview less than a year ago. Only her eyes retained their wonderfully luminous quality.

"Oh, hi," Heather said, her voice peculiarly cheerful, coming from such a ravaged body. Karen and Heather could have been two kids meeting to play a game on a quiet summer street. "Say, when are we going?"

"Going?" asked Karen. She didn't understand what Heather was talking about. "Going where, Heather?" she asked.

"To the ball game, of course! Don't you remember? To Ebbets Field. Daddy put the quart of milk in the freezer so it would still be cold when the game started. I love ice-cold milk, don't you?" Heather continued to smile inappropriately, even when Karen did not respond. Something very subtle had drained out of Heather's face. Her expression was that of an unself-conscious child.

Karen bit down on her finger, shaking. She mumbled "Oh, my God," over and over again to herself, but Heather kept smiling.

"And Daddy said I could get a pennant if I'm good." She looked puzzled. "What *is* a pennant?" she asked a bit petulantly.

"Clare!" Karen yelled, and went dashing for the door. Clare had already reached the vestibule but turned and saw a distraught Karen running toward her. "Oh, my God, Clare, I can't stand it!" she cried.

Clare was about to ask what was happening but stopped. She figured that Heather had died. She just hugged Karen tight. Karen was shaking, sweating, her heart beating out of control.

Norton came down the stairs, his slippers making a smacking noise on his feet. "What is it? What's wrong? Karen, you look faint."

Karen did not look at him but stared straight at Clare. "Please," she said finally, her voice quaking, "I don't want him to see her like this."

"It's okay, Norton," Clare said, taking control of the situation. She took him by the arm and returned to Heather.

Karen fled to the first-floor bathroom and locked herself in. "I can't stand this, I can't stand this," she repeated to herself. She turned on the cold water and splashed it on her face. She grabbed a towel and held it tight against her mouth as she screamed into it. In her head she lectured herself, hated herself. Heather and Norton need me now. I'm worse than useless! Finally she composed herself and joined then. Clare looked at her questioningly. "I'm all right now," she said. "Just stay a few minutes, okay?"

"Peanuts and candy . . ." said Heather in an almost conversational tone. "What's next?" she said to Norton.

"Should we call Dr. Kendall, do you think?" asked Norton.

"Not right away," said Clare, glancing at Karen. "We'll wait . . . to see what develops." She went over to Karen. "Are you sure you're okay now?" she whispered. Karen nodded.

"What's next?" Heather demanded petulantly.

"Crackerjacks," said Norton sadly.

" 'I don't care if I never come back,' " Heather sang, off key. Tears streamed down Norton's face.

"How long?" Karen whispered.

"Hopefully soon. It'll probably interfere with a vital function in a day or two, her breathing or her heart, and then that'll be it." Clare was a bit too clinical for Karen, but her strong spine helped to stake up her own weakness.

"What is it?" Norton asked. "She's so peculiar."

"Norton, sit down," said Karen. It was difficult for her to speak, but she felt she owed it to him. "It appears that the cancer has reached her brain."

"Oh no," said Norton. He felt sick, and leaned forward to put his head between his knees. Too late. He blacked out and tumbled forward onto the floor. Karen felt another surge of panic, but Clare was at her side.

"He's heavy, Kar'," she heard Clare saying. "Come on, help me get him on the couch in the living room. Poor man!"

"I think I'm going crazy," said Karen.

"Listen," Clare said sharply. "You're a nurse. So act like one, for God's sake. You're always lecturing the rest of us about 'real nursing.' Now here's your chance!"

Karen took hold of one of Norton's arms and helped Clare lift him onto the couch.

Norton groaned, "I'm sorry, I'm sorry."

"Do you think we should call Joan?" asked Karen.

"Good idea," said Clare, thiking to herself that Karen was unlikely to make it through the shift alone.

Karen went out into the hall and phoned. Joan was home and said she'd be right over.

"How about Ben?" Karen asked. "Should we call him too?"

"She's comfortable," said Clare. "There's really nothing he can do."

Joan was there within fifteen minutes, looking well rested. "What's up?" she asked.

Clare said, "Karen, go get Joan some fresh coffee. I'll bring her up to date."

"Is it over?" Joan asked as soon as Karen was out of earshot.

"Not yet. But her mind is gone. And Karen isn't doing well at all."

On her way back from the kitchen Karen looked in on Heather. She took one look and gasped. The eyes were open but staring backward as if examining something on the headboard. A faint smile was still on her lips. She was dead. Norton was standing numbly at the window.

Karen felt a splitting pain in her head and had a fleeting image of herself shattered into a million fragments of glass. She walked out of the room and went to tell Clare and Joan. How am I walking if I have no bones? She wondered, still caught up in her nightmare image.

Joan caught sight of her first. "Karen! Are you all right?" Karen said nothing. Clare rushed past her to see for herself what had happened. She returned a few moments later with a confused-looking Norton in tow. "She's gone," Clare said.

Karen nodded. Joan sat her friend down and said, "I'll call the hospital."

Norton buried his face in his hands and sobbed bitterly. There were tears coming down Karen's cheeks, but she remained silent. Norton mumbled something into his hands.

"What is it, Norton?" Clare asked. She wondered if she should put her arms around him, but she didn't.

"It's better," he said, lifting his head. "That was her greatest fear, to lose her mind."

Joan bit her bottom lip but kept her composure. She finally got Dr. Kendall on the phone. "I'm sorry, Doctor, but Heather Asher died this afternoon."

Hearing this out loud, Karen walked into the bedroom. Clare had covered the body with a sheet. It was very quiet, all but Norton's distant voice. Little bits of conversation reached her, familiar words, but they felt so far away now.

Karen forced herself to pull back the sheet and sat down at the edge of the bed. "Heather, I love you so much!" she said. "I promise I'll never forget what you taught me! I'll keep learning about music and literature and theater and cooking, and, and . . . I love you so, Heather!" She was finally able to cry softly. Clare and Joan came and took their friend away.

# TWELVE

## April

There was a memorial service for Heather in the upstairs room of the City Library several weeks later. Heather's body had been cremated and the ashes scattered at sea. One hundred people showed up for the services. Norton had asked Karen to say a few words, but she just couldn't bring herself to do it. Instead, many of the people who had known Heather spoke. It was a beautiful, moving ceremony, the kind of tasteful event of which Heather would have been proud.

A few weeks afterward Karen received this note from the British West Indies:

I'm back on the *Bluebonnet* as you can see. It goes without saying it's not the same without her. But I've decided to take up sailing again. I find it a great distraction. I'm actually very calm, Karen, and even when I cry—which I do a lot of—it is with a warm sort of feeling. Maybe I am just escaping from reality, but I'm continually holding little dialogues with her in my mind. And they seem so real! It's almost like she never went. Then I start to get philosophical and think that most of our lives is made up of memories anyway. So in that sense she still exists. Crazy? Well, it gets me through the day. I got a dog which I rescued from the pound—it's a long story—and we go swimming together. I think I might go to the Mediterranean again to complete the tour of North Africa which we always planned. I want to thank you again for all you did for her—for us. Heather really did love you like a daughter. I'm sad that you never knew her when she was well. Now I'm crying again! Better sign off.

    Love,
    Norton

It made her cry too. Poor Norton. He seemed so lost, so incomplete without Heather. Karen had seen many people die and had consoled many grieving relatives. Few of them had seemed so forlorn as Norton Asher. Yet Karen was sure he was going to make it.

After Heather's death Karen decided she needed a break from nursing for a while. She took off two weeks to visit her relatives, then returned to her apartment, busying herself with long-neglected chores. One morning in mid-April she was sewing a set of antique buttons onto a blouse when the phone rang.

"Hi, Karen? Got a minute?" She was happy to hear Ben's voie. They hadn't talked since she got back.

"Sure, Ben," she said. "What's up?"

"Do you think you could come in for a few days?" he asked. "I've got a case I think you'd be interested in."

"I'd rather not," she said. "I've decided I need a break since Heather died."

"Karen," he said a bit impatiently, "the best thing is to get back into the swim of things."

"Now *you're* giving me advice," she said, unable to hide

her annoyance. "You know, sometimes I wish everyone would let me make my own mistakes." She had gotten the same speech from Clare just the day before. It dismayed her how quickly everyone was willing to forget Heather.

There was silence on the other end. "Karen, I don't mean to interfere," he said finally. "Really." She could tell he was stung by her remarks.

"I thought you of all people would understand, Ben," she said more gently.

"Well, I guess it's none of my business," he said in a distant way.

She hated to think she was now driving Ben away. She liked him very much, and he only meant well. "It's your business too," she said. "I really appreciate your concern, Ben." She paused. "I'm sorry," she said, so sincerely that it cleared the air. "What kind of case is it?"

"Pediatrics," said Ben. "It's Stephanie Taylor."

"Why didn't you say so?" Karen demanded instantly. "Of course I'll come in." She was suddenly afraid. "But what is it, Ben? What's wrong? Is she getting worse?"

"Nothing like that," he said. "I'll explain to you when you come in. Do you think you could be here by, let's say, noon?"

"Are you kidding? I'll come over right now," said Karen, forgetting her previous resolve to extend her break. She put on her uniform, got into a light raincoat, and hurried through a warm, drizzling rain to the hospital. Ben was right: it was good to be back at work. When she got to the isolation unit in oncology, Ben met her outside the double swinging doors. His face lit up when he saw her and she took his hand, momentarily.

"Have you gotten a diagnosis yet? Is it AIDS?" she asked, fearing the worst.

"We still don't know," he said. "It's peculiar, but there's

still so much to learn about her problem. We even sent the blood to Atlanta to have some special tests done."

Karen glanced into the room. Stephanie was sitting up in the tent, drawing in her sketch pad. At first glance, Karen was glad to see she didn't look any worse. "What can I do?" she asked.

"We're getting the test results back today or tomorrow," he said. "I would like you to be here when they come in. Nancy and Bill Taylor have waited weeks for this, and have built up their hopes that it isn't AIDS. I try to reason with them, but they're parents. Bill Taylor asked me about private nurses because he doesn't want Stephanie to be alone."

"I understand," she said. "Thanks for recommending me, Ben," she added. "I'll go talk to Stephanie now. By the way, I'm sorry about before. I've been having a little trouble getting over Heather's death."

He smiled and shrugged his shoulders. "You'll be okay. By the way, Karen," he added, "have you given any more thought about taking a vacation at the beach? I'm still planning to go one of these days."

She smiled, and entered the isolation unit. "Hi, Stephanie," said Karen. "Remember me?"

Stephanie lifted her head and a look of delight spread over her face. "Miss Bovit!" she exclaimed. "Are you going to be my nurse now?"

"For a couple of days," said Karen, sitting down by the bed.

"Dr. Kendall told me I would have a new nurse, but he didn't say who. Do you want to see my drawings?" She held up a colorful picture of a farmhouse, a silo, some trees. "Clare asked me to draw my dream house," she exclaimed seriously. "When I grow up and get married this is the house I'm going to have in the country. See the barn? I'm going to have horses. I love horses, don't you? See the kids in the windows?" There was one child in each of the many windows.

"Are you sure you want so many children?" asked Karen. "You'll be like the old lady in the shoe."

"I'm going to have more than that. I'm also going to adopt," Stephanie said enthusiastically. Karen was relieved to see she hadn't lost any more weight.

"You're so ambitious," said Karen. "Hold it closer, Stephanie. Is that the garage? How many cars are there?" They continued talking like that for a while. There was a natural, easy rapport between them. Stephanie tired quickly, however, and soon her eyes were closing to take a nap. Karen watched until she was asleep and then slipped out of the room.

She went to the nurses' station and picked up Stephanie's chart. She was happy to see that brand-new forms had already been instituted at Riverview. The pink nurses' notes were gone. Now there was only one set of integrated notes. She made her comments directly under those of Dr. Kendall and signed her name proudly.

"Karen, could you come here for a moment?" Ben was standing with the Taylors in the vestibule. Nancy Taylor had a peculiar expression on her face—either joy or extreme grief. "Well, we got the results back from Atlanta," Ben said excitedly. "One thing is certain now. Stephanie does not have AIDS." Nancy sobbed with joy.

"What do they say it is, then?" asked Bill Taylor, muting his own happiness with a businesslike tone.

"They're not a hundred percent sure," said Ben. "It seems that Stephanie has a superinfection."

"What's that?" asked Nancy, scared again.

"A superinfection is an infection with a microorganism

that has developed a resistance to the more common antibiotics," said Ben.

"Oh yes, I read an article about that," said Mr. Taylor. "Something to do with feeding antibiotics to animals."

"That's one theory," said Ben.

"That would explain why she hasn't responded to the antibiotics, wouldn't it? But if the germ is so resistant, will she get well?" Nancy asked.

"It's a big problem," Ben admitted. "There are other drugs we haven't tried yet. Luckily, Riverview is a research center. There's an excellent lab here working on the problem. They've done amazing things in cases like this." His enthusiasm was all the more convincing because it was uncharacteristic.

"So you think they can cure her?" said Ben.

"Yes, but it's going to take some time," said Ben.

"The important thing is that it's not AIDS," Karen added.

"Stephanie is going to get better," said Nancy. "I just know she's going to be okay."

Ben and Karen felt so relieved. There weren't many question marks in the hospital. Most people were typed as soon as they came in—this one will get better, this one worse, this one will probably die. Although it never was spoken, most of the staff had already written off Stephanie as a victim of the AIDS epidemic. The Atlanta results were such a welcome surprise.

"How about walking me over to the park?" Ben asked when they finished for the day. The rain had stopped, and a golden sun had peeked through a fringe of the heavy cloud cover.

"You know, it's such a great feeling to be alive," Karen said, breathing in the clean, moist air. "It's too bad that it sometimes takes death to remind us of it." She found it so easy to talk to Ben. It was wonderful to speak her thoughts out loud, without her usual nervousness.

"Do you like kids?" Ben asked when they reached the children's zoo.

They watched some three-year-olds run up to a giant tortoise, touch it, and then run away shrieking. Karen laughed, delighted. "They're so brave, aren't they?" she asked. "That monster turtle is as big as they are."

"Don't take this the wrong way," Ben said softly. "But have you ever, you know, regretted that you never had kids?"

She looked at him in mock astonishment. "You're talking about me in the past tense! I'm still in my early thirties, you know."

"Sorry," he said awkwardly. "What I really meant to ask is, do you ever think about having kids of your own?"

"I'm sure I will," she said. "Someday."

"I think about it all the time," he said, staring straight ahead. "I think it would be wonderful."

"I guess it would," said Karen thoughtfully. "Someday," she added.

They walked on, then sat down on a bench near the small pond. They sat for a long time like that, even after night had come on. Karen hadn't done this sort of thing since high school. They talked of many things—mostly their dreams and plans. Then they ate dinner at a small restaurant. She felt she had known him all her life by the time he took her home.

Clare feared she was in for a lecture when she received the summons to Charlotte's office. But the director of nursing surprised her by being in a particularly good mood.

"I thought you would enjoy this," said Charlotte. She handed Clare a copy of a new leaflet.

In bold letters it read, "Defend Charlotte from Vicious Attacks!" They laughed together over this. The flyer contained an account of last month's board meeting. After praising Clare, the leaflet concluded:

> A real star of the event was none other than Ms. Charlotte Morgan, director of nursing. She put her former reservations aside and adopted the Rank-and-File Nurses' position on intergrated notes! There was a mass defection from the ranks of the opposition, leaving Philip the Lackey Mackey isolated and alone. The proposal passed with flying colors. Now, in a childish tantrum, Phil Mackey is trying to get Charlotte fired. We Rank-and-File Nurses demand that Lackey Mackey stop this vicious campaign of innuendo. . . .

Clare let the leaflet fall on the desk. "Well, they say politics makes strange bedfellows," she added, laughing. "Maybe they'll make us both honorary members of Rank-and-File Nurses?"

"You maybe," said Charlotte. "I'm still Monster Morgan to them. I *am* thinking of having this framed for my study, though." Clare could tell Charlotte had something else on her mind. The director came around her polished desk and sat on the corner opposite Clare. She cleared her throat. "I'm not good at speech making," Charlotte said a bit hoarsely, "so I will make this brief. Clare, I've decided to resign as director of nursing."

"What?" asked Clare, taken completely off guard.

Charlotte was amused at Clare's surprised expression. "Certainly you knew that I was considering it," she said.

Clare instantly regained her composure. "Of course, I heard the rumors. But I never expected . . . Is it because of Dr. Mackey, Charlotte?" she asked, addressing her by her given name. "Because, if it is . . . ." she added angrily.

"Phil Mackey doesn't scare me," said Charlotte, smiling. "He's all bluster. I don't think he could do much real harm if I stayed. No, this is something else. Something very personal," she added.

"I see," said Clare. "When will this take effect?" she asked.

"I've written to Dr. Stover and asked to be given a leave as of next Monday," said Charlotte.

"Next Monday!" Clare exclaimed, her heart now beating rapidly. "You're not sick, are you, Charlotte?" Clare asked.

Charlotte smiled. "No, I'm not sick. Please don't pry, Clare." She thought for a moment. "I will tell you this much. It has something to do with my family, my marriage. You see, my husband has had a heart condition for a while. I've just made a decision that I want to be home for him."

All sorts of questions and objections popped into Clare's head, but she knew not to probe any further. "is there anything I can do to ease the transition?" she asked.

Charlotte smiled broadly. "There is one small thing," she said. "I have recommended to Dr. Stover that you be made the acting director of nursing. I hope you won't refuse."

Clare was stunned. It was perfectly logical, of course, and she had often dreamed about becoming director. Yet now that it was suddenly here, she could hardly believe it. "I just don't know what to say, Charlotte," Clare stammered.

"Then don't say anything. I know we've had our disagreements over the years. But I think you're a good nurse, Clare, and a fine administrator. I hope they'll appoint you permanently as well."

"Are you sure you want to do this?" Clare asked. At that

moment she felt a surge of affection for Charlotte and hated for her to make a big mistake.

Charlotte waved her away. "Good luck, Clare." She picked up the leaflet. "Well, they won't have Monster Morgan to kick around anymore, will they?" She laughed. "Everybody make room for Horrible Henson."

On the following Monday Clare moved into the spacious nursing director's office. Over the weekend she had made two decisions. The first was that Betty would not be moving with her. The increased responsibilities would be too much for the budding novelist. To her chagrin, Betty was assigned to the typing pool while waiting for a new assignment. Her second decision walked through the door a little past eight o'clock. It was Ellen Garrison.

"I had stopped hoping for this, Ms. Henson," Ellen said. "I mean when you called me Friday . . ."

"Have a seat, Ellen," Clare said, leaning back uncertainly in what had been Charlotte's chair. It felt good. "I've given this a lot of thought. I won't say you were right in passing out those leaflets. But I believe firing you for what you did might have been excessive. And so I'm going to offer you your job back."

Ellen smiled. "I presume there are some strings attached?"

"There is one condition," Clare said seriously. "And that is that you don't ever talk about this conversation. I don't want to see a leaflet about this."

"I don't control the group," said Ellen.

It was Clare's turn to smile. "Look, Ellen," she said forcefully. "I'm sticking my neck out for you by doing this. I don't want to be embarrassed my first week on the job. You understand what I mean."

Ellen thought it over. She had another nursing job, but

the hours made it impossible for her to spend time with her daughter. In addition, the nurses' notes struggle had made her feel more a part of the hospital than she had when she worked there. "I'll talk to the other people in the group," she said finally. "For myself, I can promise you I will quit the group before I do anything to embarrass you, Ms. Henson. I really appreciate coming back to work here."

The college was located on an oak-studded hilltop in the country. Over the Easter vacation the nursing graduates always held their reunions. The ceremonies and gatherings were combined with visits to classrooms and interviews with the present-day students. Clare had protested that she was too busy with her new responsibilities to possibly attend. To her amazement, however, Joan and Karen had insisted.

As they entered the stone gates of the campus, in Clare's car, they passed under a flopping canvas sign that read R.N. PLUS TEN. WELCOME RETURNING ALUMNAE!

"Ten years! I feel like an antique," said Joan, who was sprawled on the back seat, helping herself to Mallomars.

"Will you go easy on those things?" asked Clare, glancing in the mirror. "You're blowing up like a zeppelin."

"You're one to talk, tubby," said Joan automatically. With chocolate on her face she looked like a kid, and Karen had to smile.

They wound their way up the campus drive, Joan leaning forward and yelling, "Turn here! Turn here!"

"Have you ever seen so many potholes in your life?" Karen asked as she jolted in her seat. "No wonder they're always begging us for money."

"What a horrible mistake. To spend money on education

when they could be repairing potholes," Joan drawled humorously.

"Are you sure you remember the way, Joan?" Clare whined. "I'm completely lost now. They seem to have rearranged the place since I was last here."

"It's you that's changed," said Joan seriously. "Stop that child and ask her." They got directions from a young student. "Did you get a load of her? Freckles and braces! I can't take this. What century am I from? Could we possibly have looked like that?" Joan gave an idiot grin, which was actually a vicious but devastating imitation of the student's happy expression. She had Karen in stitches.

"I can see what kind of weekend this is going to be," Clare said, laughing.

They finally found the dormitory—a vine-covered brick building. A student sat at a desk. "Welcome home," she said cheerfully. Each of them was given an orientation packet and a name tag. The name tags had "happy faces" on them.

Clare held the "happy face" up to her own. "Mrs. Beecher," she whispered, and Joan shrieked. The student looked at them with amusement.

They made their way down the corridors, which were damp and smelled of chlorine bleach, and unlocked their room. It was dark until Clare pulled the stiff curtains, and then the sunlight flooded in. Everything was cheerful, functional, and screwed down to the floor.

Joan said, "I've got dibs on this," and threw her duffle bag onto the one single bed. Clare magnanimously took the top bunk. Joan spread her stuff out and quickly monopolized the bathroom shelves with her cosmetics and junk.

Clare slid open the windows and breathed in the fresh country air. "This is the kind of air that makes me think of fresh country eggs and sausages."

"Do you think Allen Eastlake's going to be here?" asked Joan.

"Allen Eastlake's gay," said Clare, hanging her blouses in the closet.

"Which only shows how horny I am," Joan yelled from the bathroom.

Karen smiled. She was thinking of her last walk with Ben in the park—how nice the spring could be, in the city or the country, when you were happy.

After showering and switching into fresh clothes they went for a walk on the campus. The students who hadn't gone home for spring break rode around on bicycles or walked in pairs.

"Isn't this weird?" said Joan. "You know, I haven't been back in ten years."

"Me neither," said Karen.

"I come up now and then," said Clare. "I spoke here a couple of years ago."

"In a way, nothing has changed," said Joan. "Except us." They walked past the lecture hall. "Let's go look at our old dorm." It was a boxlike building, thrown up for the baby boomers. "Want to go inside?"

"Not really," said Karen. "It's embarrassing."

"Remember when that woman came and took pictures? She had lived in the room," said Joan. "It seemed so pathetic. I vowed I'd never be like that. Hey, did you bring your camera?"

They peered into the hallway. "I don't remember that the corridors were so narrow," said Clare. "Do you remember when they had the sorority rush?" she asked.

"Ugh!" said Joan, making a face. "I hate sororities. Don't ever mention them to me."

"Mrs. Beecher did away with them last year," said Clare.

"How about the egg-throwing contest?" asked Joan. "And that girl who got 'eau de skunk' on her suede jacket?"

"That was you, Joan, wasn't it?" Karen teased.

"Me?" Joan asked indignantly. "I was into other things. And they were into me," she added.

They skipped the get-together smorgasbord and wandered into town. There was only one place to go, and that was Willy's Pub. The three of them found a table in the crowded pub and sat down. "I don't believe this," Karen screamed, continuing the mood of hysteria. "They still have the same seats." Willy's motif was maritime— portholes, lobster traps, and nets, although Willy's was hundreds of miles from the sea. To fit in with the motif, the "chairs" were made of barrels of grog sawed in half.

"These damn rims left permanent grooves in my behind," said Joan, settling in. "I'm not kidding! That's why I have such a peculiar shape."

Karen giggled and ordered a large order of Willy's famous french fries and, without thinking, a pitcher of beer.

"Not for me," said Joan quickly. "I'll have a diet soda, thanks."

"Well, I am impressed," said Clare. Joan gave a little bow.

The drinks arrived and Joan proposed a toast. "To the new director of nursing," she said, raising her ginger ale. "Long may she wave."

Clare waved. "Good thing it's so dark in here," she said, "so you can't see me blushing. Please. I'm not the director yet. Only acting."

"Only acting? You could have fooled me," said Joan. "Look, Clare. You've got Charlotte's recommendation to the board. You're a shoo-in."

Clare smiled. "There's still a search committee," she said judiciously. "And your friend Phil Mackey is on it."

"On no," Karen groaned.

"I can't help you in that department," said Joan. "Grandpa and I have had a total parting of the ways."

"You know, Joan, I don't think that's any great loss," Karen said. "Don't answer if you don't want to. But what did you ever see in him?"

"Oh, I don't know. Well, for one thing, he always bought the drinks. He made me feel secure."

"You felt insecure?" asked Karen, who had always envied her friend's sex appeal.

"Sure. Why do you think people drink, you idiot? I was on shaky ground. Mackey was one of my crutches. That's over now."

"I guess I can tell you now," Clare said hesitantly. "Phil Mackey tried to get me to fire you."

Joan tried to remain unaffected, but she wasn't. "That hardly surprises me. What a son of a bitch," she added in a low voice. "Guys. You can't live with 'em and you can't live without 'em. All except Karen here. She's proved them wrong. She lives without 'em. Right, Karen?" Karen laughed easily at Joan's teasing.

"Okay, enough of this," said Clare, intervening. "We're here to have a good time. Joan, finish up your ginger ale. The next round's on me!"

Saturday was taken up attending seminars and seeing old classmates. Allen Eastlake, one of the few male nurses in their class, did indeed ask Joan out on a date. She surprised everyone by turning him down. "I can't stand the smell of his cologne," she whispered to Karen. Actually, she just wanted to stay with her friends. They had fun talking to the young students. It was so easy to remember themselves at this age, eager and enthusiastic, filled with the high ideals of their profession.

On Sunday there was the big convocation for the alumnae, faculty, and students. They all gathered in the dining hall, draped with foreign flags, which doubled as school auditorium.

Mrs. Beecher, who had been their nursing ethics teacher, was now dean of studies. She had seemed old when they had her ten years before. Since she was only in her fifties now, they recognized their misperception. After handing out various medals and awards to the students, she paused.

"It is our tradition," she said, "to honor that graduate of our school who has done the most to advance the cause of the nursing profession in the ten years since graduation. We know all of you have brought credit to this school, even if we've lost touch with some of you for a time."

"This is just like being back in school," Karen whispered. Joan smiled.

"As I look around this sea of faces," Mrs. Beecher added slowly, "I begin to remember you one by one. Naturally, we are all a bit older. . . . Some of us are a bit wiser. Others are a bit larger." The audience gave the obligatory chuckles. "The Founder's Day Award, which we are about to announce, has been called the Academy Award of Nursing. This year the choice for the Committe was not very difficult. One only needs to watch the television or listen to the radio to know what I mean."

She opened the envelope in front of her with a letter opener.

"And so, without further ado, the winner of this year's award"—she paused meaningfully— "is our own Clare Henson, acting director of nursing at Riverview Hospital!" There was loud applause, the loudest from Joan and Karen.

Clare was thunderstruck. She had had absolutely no idea

this was coming. But when she looked at Joan and Karen she gasped. "You both knew!" she cried angrily. "I'll get you for this!" she whispered.

Mrs. Beecher beckoned her to the stage when the applause subsided.

"As you all know, Clare waged a determined struggle to integrate the doctors' and the nurses' notes into one form at Riverview. This is a cause I think she first advocated in my nursing ethics class ten years ago." Karen and Joan laughed, at Mrs. Beecher's obvious attempt to share the glory. Clare had reached the podium. "And so, the university welcomes you home, Clare, and presents you with this plaque and with a check for one thousand dollars as a token of our appreciation."

Clare thanked her and took the award; the applause surrounded and overwhelmed her. She was too choked up to give a speech. Karen and Joan hugged her, and there were tears on her cheeks now—both theirs and hers. She couldn't wait to call Ken. This reunion had recognized her new career as director. Her joy was tinged with sadness, because every beginning was also an ending as well.

It was already dark when they started out for home that evening. Karen drove. There was no time for the scenic route, and they sped along the boring interstate. Finally they drove into the city, and Joan woke as they pulled up in front of Karen's apartment. Karen shut off the engine and stretched.

"What time is it?" Joan asked drowsily.

"Just past midnight," said Karen.

"Oh, God," Joan said. "What a long drive."

"What are you complaining about? I've still got to drive home," said Clare.

"Thanks, guys. I had a great time, really," said Joan. "By the way, I've decided to come back to work this week.

I actually miss the unit. Can't wait to see Sarah and Bijan. Congratulations again, Clare." She kissed her on the cheek. "We're so proud of you."

"Thanks, Joan," said Clare. "And the check will sure come in handy. Ken's decided to take a new job next week. It's a real cut in pay, but he'll be helping to build a small company from the bottom up. And there's a good chance for advancement."

Karen got out.

"And what about you, Karen?" Clare asked, sliding behind the wheel. "See you tomorrow?"

"I don't think so," Karen said slowly.

"Still feeling burnt out?" Clare asked. "I have an interesting case for you, if you want it."

"No, that won't be necessary," Karen replied a bit mysteriously. "As a matter of fact, I'm planning to take a little vacation."

"Something exciting, like painting your apartment?" asked Joan, sharing a joke with Clare.

"Really, Kar'?" asked Clare, who was better attuned to the nuances in Karen's voie.

"Really. I'm leaving tomorrow night. And I'm quite excited about it, too." Her face glowed in the lamplight.

"Where you going, Karen? The Virgin Islands?" asked Joan, laughing.

"You're not too far off, Joan," Karen said good-naturedly. "The Bahamas."

"That sounds nice," said Joan, but she sounded puzzled.

Clare's face suddenly lit up with recognition. "Wait one minute!" she demanded. "Didn't Ben Kendall tell me he's also going to the Bahamas?"

"Oh, is he?" Karen asked innocently.

"Are you kidding!" Joan exclaimed, finally catching on.

"I can't believe this. Are you going with him, Karen?" asked Clare.

"Maybe I'll see him down there. Who knows?" Karen said with a broad smile.

"Maybe there's hope for you yet," Joan said with amazement.

"So," said Karen. There was an awkward pause. "You know, this was a great weekend. Do you realize it was just a year ago that we found each other again?"

"What a long year," said Joan.

"Long? It just flew by," said Clare.

"I wonder where we'll all be ten years from now," said Karen.

"I'm really looking forward to being director of nursing. I think I'm going to get the job," she confided. "It makes me so nervous, though. How about you, Joan?"

"Maybe I'll go back to school after all," said Joan. "I don't know. I hate to admit it, but I think my drinking may have screwed up my academic career . . . and my marriage."

Karen laughed. "I'm going to concentrate more on my personal life. Starting tomorrow."

"Well, I've got work tomorrow," said Clare, impatient to get on the road. "Can I drop you at home?" she asked Joan.

"No," said Joan slowly. "Just drop me at that bar up the street." They looked at her astounded. "Just kidding."

"You know, Clare," said Karen slowly, "there's something I've been wanting to say to you for a long time."

"Uh-oh, a speech," said Joan, closing her eyes.

Karen smiled but wasn't deterred. "No, I'm serious. I'm really glad you won that award today, because I think you deserve it. What I mean is, I was really proud of you, the way you acted last month . . . with Heather."

"And what about me?" asked Joan, opening her eyes.

"You too, Joan. You guys were really terrific. Which is another way of saying, I'm sorry about how I carried on about 'real nursing' I always seem to get overinvolved."

Clare thought for a moment before answering. "Sometimes I envy you for your involvement. It's your greatest asset. Don't ever change."

Karen smiled warmly.

"Now get out of here," Clare said roughly, "before you have *me* breaking down and slobbering."

"Fat chance of that," said Joan. "You've taken to your new role like a duck to water. Horrible Henson. Come on, Kar'. Let's get out of here. We're simply outclassed."

They both got out and walked down the street, talking animatedly. Joan put her arm through Karen's as they walked. Clare sat for a minute in the darkness, watching her friends go. It was a bittersweet moment. Then she turned the key in the ignition, shifted into gear, and swiftly drove away.

# _New York Times_ bestsellers— Berkley Books at their best!

___ 0-425-10005-7 **THE EIGHTH COMMANDMENT**  $4.95
by Lawrence Sanders
Sex, corruption, scandal...A priceless Greek coin is stolen
and another priceless Sanders suspense is born!

___ 0-425-10107-X **RED STORM RISING**  $4.95
by Tom Clancy   (On sale 8/87)
A frightening real superpower battle. The explosive
superthriller by the author of _The Hunt For Red October._

___ 0-425-09633-5 **THE LEBARON SECRET**  $4.50
by Stephen Birmingham
Glittering wealth, consuming ambition and shattering secrets,
from America's favorite chronicler of the rich and famous.

___ 0-425-09884-2 **STONE 588**  $4.50
by Gerald A. Browne
A valuable gemstone drives men and women to obsession
and murder. "Dazzling!" —New York _Daily News_

___ 0-425-10237-8 **"AND SO IT GOES"**  $4.50
by Linda Ellerbee
"Funny, honest stuff that's all too revealing about how T.V.
works." —_People_

___ 0-515-08793-7 **BESS W. TRUMAN**  $4.50
by Margaret Truman
A triumphant and intimate portrayal of the remarkable
First Lady—as only her daughter could tell it.

# There's an epidemic with 27 million victims. And no visible symptoms.

It's an epidemic of people who can't read.

Believe it or not, 27 million Americans are functionally illiterate, about one adult in five.

The solution to this problem is you... when you join the fight against illiteracy. So call the Coalition for Literacy at toll-free **1-800-228-8813** and volunteer.

## Volunteer Against Illiteracy. The only degree you need is a degree of caring.